There is a way of making free with the past,
a pastiche of what is real and what is not,
which can only be justified if you think of it
not as sculpture but syntax.

Eavan Boland: 'Lava Cameo'

Preface

This book tells the story of Margaret Fell's life but it is not biography. I have tried to walk alongside this seventeenth-century woman that I might begin to know her.

Margaret Fell (1614-1702) was an English gentlewoman. She belonged to a generation that fought a civil war and executed a king for reasons that had as much to do with religion as they did with politics. Against the backdrop of revolution, men and women questioned the nature of their relationship with God, and the need, or lack of need, for an established church. They explored new ways of worship and looked for guidance to new prophets.

In the mid-1640s, George Fox, son of a Leicestershire weaver, a restless, questing spirit, answered God's demand that he 'gather a great people'. These Children of Light or Friends of Truth, as they were known, were no mere sect: they were 'a people' called by God to live out His truth on earth. Fox's was a mystical religion, which avowed that the Light of God was present for, and in, each individual believer. He rejected priests and formal prayer: his followers met in silence and their silence was met by the light and spirit of a living God whose power might compel them to quake or speak or sing in acknowledgement of His presence and their obedience. The name Quaker was coined to abuse men and women who could shake uncontrollably in worship. It survived, part of the legacy Fox's generation bequeathed to their spiritual descendants in the present day Religious Society of Friends.

The ungodly ridiculed Fox's followers and the law hounded them. Yet thousands were convinced (Fox's term for conversion). They formed a church or a 'people' whose lives were dedicated to God but whose calling was to live in the world rather than the cloister. 'The world' was contemporary society, worldly in the worst sense, removed from God and therefore evil. It was a world of darkness, to which George Fox would bring the light of God. His people must preach God's truth in their England without being defiled by the manners and morals of the day. The determination to live as God demanded and not as the world expected made early Quakers dangerously visible. Not to remove one's hat in greeting, not to use titles and keep to the familiar 'thee' and 'thou' when addressing a person of rank, to refuse to pay the tithe or church tax, to refuse to swear an oath in a court of law, were all confrontational actions. This was no easy path! Yet thousands of English women and men walked it, sure that simplicity, or purity, of life would bring them closer to God. It was God who forced them to strip their lives of 'cumber', the clutter of worldly aspirations and values.

They were impelled to give voice to their faith, preaching in streets or in 'steeple houses', as they called the churches, interrupting sermons and services, risking attack from angry crowds. They feared neither arrest nor mob violence, stoically accepting suffering as part of God's plan. Their constant defiance of their enemies was outrageous to the point of lunacy: it was also provocative. So were some of their acts of witness. There were Quakers who were called to 'go naked for a sign', stripping to the skin in the market place in response to the will of God, and protest against the world's falsity.

In 1652 Margaret Fell, aged thirty-eight, wife to a judge and mother of seven children, was convinced by George Fox. Her wealth and social standing, her energy and the strength of her commitment made her a natural leader. Legend claims her as 'the mother of Quakerism'. A seemingly conventional seventeenth century gentlewoman broke bounds to become the 'mother' of social and legal outcasts. Why?

This book is my search for an answer. In writing it I went on a journey through another woman's life and through my own.

Writing is a solitary task but spiritual journeys are rarely made alone. This book owes an enormous debt to the people whose lives have touched mine during its writing. In writing it I travelled from one faith community to another. I am deeply thankful for both the Quaker meeting that sustained the journey's beginning and the parish church that sustains me now. The book began as a project for

Woodbrooke's 'Equipping for Ministry' course. Without the support of Woodbrooke staff and students it would not have progressed very far. Thank you. And thank you especially to all those friends who read (and even re-read!) the text in any or all of its drafts. Without their encouragement I may well have given up. Lastly, thank you to my family who viewed my retreat into another century with a kindly tolerance. This book is for Martin who lived, and still lives, with two women.

* * * * *

Thursday, 1st July 1652: market day in Ulverston. In the square they traded on for coppers and small silver regardless of the summons to church. Cottagers' wives, who counted survival in farthings and half pence, willed butter not to turn in the heat. A beggar urinated in the gutter. Livestock bellowed, the noise belying their skeletal frames. A drunkard raised a flagon of ale to his great slobbering mouth and called obscenities after a serving maid. The reply came in kind, the crude banter of the streets, but the laughter of the bystanders had an uneasy edge to it. The day was sultry. Tempers would fray. Bargaining would become bickering; fists would be raised. Those who played out life's small dramas here by day, would go home, to sweat the night out in the low rooms of cottages where privacy, love and passion were all snatched in seconds.

Less than two miles away, at Swarthmoor Hall on the edge of the town, a woman dressed for church with fastidious care. Ordering her appearance might help order her thoughts. Her movements had a slow deliberation that concealed emotion as she fumbled momentarily with the chain of a necklace and finally clicked home the clasp. Her hand rested on the oval of gold at her throat with its painted image of a man. The living man was away dispensing justice. Did she regret his absence or not? Unable to answer the question, she took a last look at her mirrored self and, satisfied, moved towards the door. The carriage would take her and the children to Ulverston. Despite the heat she wanted the privacy of the enclosed space behind the Fell coat of arms. She needed protection from chance conversations and questions that would catch her unprepared.

Margaret Fell climbed into the carriage and left her son and daughters to follow. She only half noticed the continuing quarrels that threatened to erupt about window space and foot room. The absence of reproof or interest made the children uncomfortable. An uneasy quiet prevailed until the younger ones caught sight of the peddler with the crooked face, his skin etched and mapped by smallpox, and craned forward. For once there was no maternal objection to their curiosity. Margaret was locked in her own thoughts. Her older daughters wanted to break the barrier of silence but didn't know how. The last minutes of the brief journey were becoming uncomfortably long. The carriage came to a halt and jolted Margaret into awareness. The groom opened the door: the bustle of leaving provided a release from tension. The young Fells gained the freedom of the church path and waited awkwardly for their mother.

St. Mary's church stood sheltered under the hill, secluded from the work-a-day busyness and dirt of the town. Mistress Fell shepherded her children towards its open door. The building offered the godly no respite from the heat, just a clammy shade. Margaret took the deep breath that might prelude calm. A composed exterior and a gracious smile were necessary accessories for a woman of rank. Offering polite greetings to a tenant here and a tradesman there she made her way to the front of the church, to the pew that went with social standing and the size of the Swarthmoor estate. This was an England in which your place in church reflected your place in society. The gentry sat to the fore; behind them were the tenant farmers and more substantial tradesmen of the town; right at the back, by the door, crowded the household servants and day labourers.

Safe once more from neighbourly curiosity, Margaret tried again to calm her own mind. She did not want to admit how far she had been disturbed by what she rationalised as a brief meeting with an itinerant preacher who would be gone again tomorrow. She had to keep face in this community where her life lay. For now she must play her allotted roles: Swarthmoor's lady, Thomas's wife, her children's mother, her servants' mistress. She turned and retied Sarah's bonnet strings with a force that the hot, uncomfortable ten-year old found impossible to resist. Her son George, at fourteen none too sure what was expected of him in his father's absence, threatened to begin an unrhythmical tapping of one foot against the other. His eyes caught his mother's and he stopped. An uneasy peace settled.

Judge Fell's absence from home was common knowledge. The respect he was accorded locally included a certain amount of wariness if not fear. Thomas Fell's star was in the ascendant in Oliver Cromwell's England and his neighbours were not sure how far it would rise. The judge's influence had secured the living of St. Mary's for William Lampit two years before, but he did not regard himself as bound by Lampit's ministry. Swarthmoor's hospitality and its master's attention were readily and regularly given to itinerant ministers. Thomas Fell had yet to find his own truth; meanwhile he explored everyman's. George Fox's arrival at the Hall the day before had been unremarkable in itself. The interest lay in his meeting with the Reverend Lampit that had ended in an angry clash of temperaments and theologies. William Lampit's congregation prayed for divine mercy and expected human drama. The stranger had been seen pacing the fields between Swarthmoor and the town. Soon he must feel the pull of the steeple house. Some were already prepared to denounce him as lunatic or sorcerer.

William Lampit entered from the vestry, a man conscious of his own dignity and that of his office. This was his church. This was his flock. He looked round, tight-lipped, authoritative. His congregation composed hearts, minds and countenances. Hats and hands were used to fan florid country faces. This Thursday lecture was part of a pattern of public worship that tried to use the power of prayer, sermon and religious exercise as a bulwark against national disasters. In a country that had suffered the ravages of civil war and five years of bad harvest, the spread of cynicism now seems unsurprising. Yet to some, God's apparent indifference was a sign that they should try harder to purge their consciences and regiment their lives in the hope of full bellies and orderly government.

William Lampit, stern man and convinced Puritan that he was, carried his congregation in the wake of his own conscience. What did Priest Lampit choose as his text? Jeremiah?

> We acknowledge, O Lord, our wickedness, and the iniquity of our fathers: for we have sinned against thee. Do not abhor us, for thy name's sake, do not disgrace the throne of thy glory: remember break not thy covenant with us.

The minister had a reputation as 'a warm and lively preacher' but there was no time for a scholarly or even a passionate discussion of God's covenant with his people and its breach. Fox erupted into the church while Lampit was still leading the singing of metrical psalms, a monotonous, repetitive recital of scripture, intended to edify rather than uplift. This was the moment people had been anticipating. As the dull ring of metal-toed boots on stone was heard in the porch a score of necks craned towards the entrance. The heavy wooden door lurched open. There was no question of tact or ceremony, as one William Lampit's flock shuffled and twisted in its seats hoping for a better view. They were half prepared for the odd appearance of the man who now propelled himself into their midst; the leather clothing and the long ill-kempt hair under the broad-brimmed white hat. They were totally unprepared for the fire in his voice, or for the power of his inspirations. Fox could both enrage and magnetise. John Sawrey, magistrate and gentleman land-owner of Plumpton Hall, could scarce contain his desire to have the newcomer forcibly removed from the church. Justice Sawrey, red-faced and near exploding with rage and self importance, was conscious of the need for leadership by a man of rank and status. More than one of his neighbours suspected that he might be taking an unholy satisfaction in the opportunity afforded him by Judge Fell's absence. William Lampit, gaining stature and a certain amount of physical protection from his pulpit, tried to remain aloof from the situation. The clergyman was conciliatory, yesterday's anger laid aside. He clung to his lectern and his determination to play the rational man. Margaret's intervention changed the focus of the drama. She rose to her feet and the action had the impact of the unexpected. The shadow of the judge's office rose beside her as Sawrey and Lampit turned in her direction. Margaret's eyes met John Sawrey's. He could not hold her stare. Discomfited and discountenanced he lowered his bulk into the nearest pew. He wanted no more eye contact with this woman and his reasons had nothing to do with the judicial authority of Thomas Fell. The incident was over. Lampit regained control of the situation and ceded the pulpit to Fox.

Margaret sank back into her seat. Sawrey mopped sweat from his brow, let his indignation simmer and prayed that his moment would come. It had taken less than a minute. For Margaret that was the beginning, despite all the words that remained to be said.

Why had she allowed herself to become visible? She recognised the will of God. She answered Fox's need. She accepted her own destiny. But why? Eventually she recorded her life's history, but by then the beginning didn't seem to matter very much. It was all so long ago. The young mother with a clutch of small children, the woman who was Thomas's lover, the bride seeing Swarthmoor for the first time, the child at Marsh Grange: who were they? They stood in the shadows of the old woman's memory. They were too much a part of her to be worth recording but they stood behind her in Ulverston church.

* * * * *

> I was born in the year 1614, at Marsh Grange, in the parish of Dalton in Fournis in Lancashire.

I went to look for the house. Once it was an Elizabethan manor built to give its owners the space and comfort that goes with rank of the middling sort. The men who lived there were gentlemen farmers: they had no need to dirty their hands with manual work, but they were not so well off that they could consign all their affairs to a steward. They managed their estates, kept a check on market prices, decided when to add to their herds and when cattle should be sold for leather or meat. This thin ribbon of land between Duddon Sands and the high country moor was never a hospitable place for a dwelling. Its inhabitants lived with the changing moods of the sea and the hills. The twentieth century house is surrounded by a medley of farm and domestic litter. Its rendered façade and dull paint-work present a blank face to the world and the weather. The owners are hostile to the chance visitor or idle tourist looking for access to the beach. Chained farm dogs bark. 'No Parking' is daubed in uneven black painted letters on the yard wall. Another sign demands that you beware of children although today's children are no more visible than those of three centuries ago. There is continuity of occupation in the rusting machinery, the cattle grazing near the house, the sheep on the slopes, but repeated layers of history have altered the landscape. The railway to Barrow, legacy of a more recent, industrial past, cuts the house off from the sea. Ranks of modern windmills look down from a distant hillside. Heavy lorries rush along the tarmac of the Dalton road.

Margaret Fell's Dalton was a prosperous market town. 'A good market for all kinds of Provisions, seated in a champain country not farr from ye sea' wrote Daniel Fleming in 1671. Now its centre carries the stamp of poverty: boarded-up windows display nothing but posters for yesterday's sales and the scrawled fantasies of today's young. Donna loves Gavin, or lusts after him, or fancied him for a week last summer. Bargain basement shops survive a few weeks as the 'Garden Store' or 'Christmas World'. Behind steamy windows a café serves tea in thick china mugs with scones that are doorsteps of carbohydrate. A huddle of hillside houses shelters a community whose purpose seems lost. The creaking pub sign of The Miners' Arms forges a tenuous link with industrial history. On the hill, a woman toils past me, baby and buggy festooned with carrier bags. Behind, an anorak-wrapped toddler doggedly sucks on Mickey Mouse recast as a lurid lollipop.

Across the peninsula, tucked away on the southern edge of Ulverston, Swarthmoor maintains its claim to be country rather than town. The footpath between the two is rural enough once you leave the primary school and the last bungalows behind, although the October sunshine has the space occupied by the town's dog walkers. At the stream the stone bridge is being repaired. The narrow walk-way left free of scaffolding offers little room to stand and stare but there is a sense of crossing from one world to another. Stream and meadow have their own kind of quiet. The track from the footpath to the road once served the hall as an entrance for farm carts and tradesmen's drays. Outbuildings butt the wall between house and track. Moss grows in the tiles of roofs and old brickwork crumbles. The house itself narrowly escapes dilapidation. Lived in, it's not quite a home. Enshrined, it's not quite a museum. On Swarthmoor Lane a lycra-clad jogger disappears into the distance leaving only the deserted road behind. A straggly clump of red campion still blooms in the hedge. Beyond the hall gates I glimpse the dull brittle pink of summer's last hydrangeas. At the entrance a notice fades in time and mood with the house. The hall is closed to visitors and I am invited to telephone. Later I do, and the impersonal friendliness of an answer-phone offers to call me back but such promises are not for the transient. I let it go, relieved. I want to peel away the layers of this house with its cracked render and unremarkable exterior but I don't want to find the mythology. I want to find the woman who lived here three hundred years ago. It is the spirits of the past I'm looking for, not today's wardens.

I retrace my steps across the bridge and along the footpath and try to get the measure of Ulverston. It has fared better than Dalton from passing time. Virtually nothing remains of the seventeenth-century church. Victorian confidence and Victorian wealth gave today's St. Mary's its solid dignity. The building is locked, its porch shuttered. Against its walls the pale fragile stems of autumn crocuses support a sweep of mauve flower heads. A gardener painstakingly clips the churchyard hedge. It's a well-kept, silent, almost empty space. Today's powerhouse is not the church but the parish centre opposite with its busy notice boards and open door. Cattle graze on Hoad Hill, as they must always have done. The Barrow monument stands grimly on its summit, remarkable more for the plainness of its construction than any architectural beauty. I gratefully accept the shelter it offers from the wind and look down on the town and its past.

> The canal, a mile and a half in length, which con-nects the town with the sea, was constructed in 1794, and led to a considerable increase in the shipping trade; it was a remarkable work in its time, but the opening of the railway and the docks of Barrow have long rendered it practically use-less. Recently at the sea end, Canal Foot, and at Sand Side villages have sprung up, iron furnaces having been constructed there in 1876, and a paper factory and a chemical works also. There are tanneries and corn mills in the town, and minor industries, including the making of patent shutters.

So recorded the *Victoria County History* in 1911.

At Plumpton, where the railway now crosses the sands on the solid iron way of a viaduct, John Sawrey's house can still be seen. Its silhouette is a replica of Marsh Grange and Swarthmoor but this house is gilded with today's prosperity. An unknown architect has converted its barn into twin suburban residences displaying identical candy-floss shades of petunias in window boxes and hanging baskets. Seabirds reel and call on a shoreline tamed by our search for quiet.

Summer visitors come here to walk the fells or visit Ulverston's Laurel and Hardy museum. Tourism is a major industry now, although year-round employment is provided by the Glaxo factory, a metallic wonderland almost at the sea's edge. The town seems to have little use for its dilapidated railway station where grass grows raggedly through the cracked tarmac of platforms, and deserted buildings have long since been declared redundant.

Arriving by train you understand the isolation that gave 'Lancashire beyond the Sands' its identity. These tracks were laid to carry iron ore out of Furness in a time of prosperity and full employment. Then the Furness Railway and the towns it served kept up appearances with fresh paint and newly planted window boxes. Now all they do is survive. At Carnforth, town and railway decline together: paint peels and graffiti gathers. Travellers once shared tables and life histories in this skeleton of a station buffet. Now, even the ghosts have gone. A huge round clock hangs above the platforms. On some long forgotten day it stopped at twenty past three. At Arneside, the tide is on the ebb and the train strikes out across a wasteland of quick sands and mudflats, where sea birds gather to feed, and the only sound is the persistent call of the gulls. The empty landscape holds its own mystery, and its own danger, that together weave the magic of place.

* * * * *

Once, long ago, in the wild time at the back end of the year…

The old one came over the sands alone. The wind had veered round to the north; the waves reached to more than a man's height. Rain blew almost horizontally across the bay. The year was dying. The day was so dark you could scarce see. Still the crazy figure wove its way across the quicksands and the river channels. Depths and shallows were complete uncertainties in weather like this. The Keer and the Leven were both running high. The bay could flood in less time than it would take the fool to confess its sins and ask forgiveness of its maker. But still the figure moved on, circling and reeling, uttering strange cries. Protected by God or led by the devil, it found the Ulverston shore. Folk out early to lament the storm damage saw the ancient huddled on the beach, drenched sacking its only protection from the cold. They crossed themselves and stared at the stranger, muttering about witchcraft and blame for the anger of the elements. The old one seemed oblivious to their presence. One goodman tried a prod with his staff. Another, braver, fellow touched the huddle of flesh and bone with the toe of his boot. For an instant a grim gaunt face stared back at the small group, its eyes stricken like a cowered animal. The stranger moaned and wailed and shuffled upright. The goodfolk followed its unsteady progress through the town. They jeered and pointed and cursed and crossed themselves for protection. The following became driving. They forced the wild demented soul out beyond the last habitation until, still weaving and reeling its way, still calling incoherently to the wind, it found the open moor. They let it go, thanking God they were done with it, and trudged homewards, inventing excuses and justifications.

And the outcast? Eventually it came to a solitary rest in the abandoned byre at the edge of the marsh by Duddon Sands. The people let it be. There was little to be gained from taunting a creature this removed from comfort and company and some sensed there might be danger.

* * * * *

There are no easy explanations for death and suffering. We can't explain away our own anguish no matter how hard we try. With the passing of time we've got better at causes. Disease and the crop failure that leads to famine have become understandable and to some extent controllable. Margaret's generation had no explanation but the will of God. Plague and famine were acts of divine providence sent by God to chastise his people. God's people needed to know the cause of his displeasure. They examined their consciences; then they looked at the strangers or outsiders in their midst and cried witchcraft or sorcery. We might wonder at their ignorance but we can hardly condemn it. They lived more closely with death than us. Of the children born in 1614, the year of Margaret Fell's birth, a quarter did not survive past their tenth birthday. Most of the deaths came within the first year of life. Bereaved families and infant burials were a commonplace. Epidemics were fierce, frequent and unchecked. Bubonic plague reached Kendal in 1598 and over a thousand people died within three months, half the population of this small town. There was no one who escaped without losing friend or relative. It was the whole community who suffered and the whole community who felt the wrath of a God whose image was power and anger rather than love. Little wonder they looked for scapegoats. Little wonder they distrusted strangers and moved vagrants on. They had so little security. If the crops failed two years in succession England suffered famine. There were bad years in virtually every decade and there were outstandingly bad years. 1587-88, 1597 and 1623 lived in folk memory as years of tight belts and the continuous trek of coffin-laden carts from cottage to churchyard. Some reverted to the old ways, wanting the gospel read in the cornfields to encourage the crops to grow and talking of witches.

* * * * *

It seemed to the child that the old one had been there forever, wandering the shore and the marsh, always alone. She thought of the magic of witches and cunning folk. She knew about the offerings laid at the byre door: a loaf of black bread, a few eggs, a dead rabbit. She didn't know, any more than the donors, whether the gifts were given in charity or fear. She enjoyed the shivers the tale produced. Very slowly and deliberately she made the sign of the cross.

From the beginning Margaret knew about the land's magic. She knew witchcraft was real despite the calm disbelief with which her father treated the subject. She frightened herself with the stories of the common folk. She knew about the Purgatory Field, where families met to pray for their dead, to keep them out of Hell and speed their way to Heaven. She'd seen the fires burning there on All Saints Eve.

When she was older, the child learned the land's history. Long, long ago Stephen, Count of Boulogne and Mortain, Lord of Lancaster, gave this land to the monks of Savigny in Normandy.

> The forest and desmesne of Furness, the manor of Ulverston, the land of Roger Brentwald, the Count's fishery in the Lune by Lancaster and Warin the Little with his land.

White-robed Cistercians came here from France The people of the land accepted these strangers who had the blessing of the prince and the church. They respected the austerity and the power of the abbey. Their lives took their rhythm from the feasts of the church year and the order of mass for the day. Latin prayers were offered to a God at once familiar and mysterious.

> *Ecce Agnus Dei, ecce qui tollit peccata mundi.*
> *Domine, non sum dignus ut intres sub tectum meum:*
> *sed tantum dic verbo, et sanabitur anima mea.*

And so it was for nearly four hundred years in which the abbey became more powerful and the monks less austere. A king, who wanted to rule the church as well as the land and its people, coveted the wealth and power and condemned the loss of faith. The abbey was dissolved and its land passed to those who had the means to buy it. It was then that her great grandfather bought Marsh Grange. Or he might have done. For what do we know of Margaret's family?

> My father's name was John Askew, he was of ancient family, of those esteemed and called gentlemen, who left a considerable estate, which had been in his name and family for several generations. He was a pious, charitable man, and patient, and was bred after the best way and manner of persons of his rank and day.

Of her mother she says nothing.

John Askew married Margaret Pyper in February 1613. The names are too common and the parish registers too incomplete for history to be certain that this is the right couple, but the dates fit and they will serve. Let us add a little flesh to these bare facts. Within a year of his marriage John Askew came into his father's fortune and the couple moved into Marsh Grange. It is the only home his daughters have known. Margaret's father is a quietly pious man, mindful of his responsibilities to his household, his tenants and the land he has inherited. He is a good steward of his estate and his fortune and, as befits a good steward, he approaches change cautiously. His politics and religion are conservative. In Jacobean England he remains an Elizabethan. (He was born in 1580 or thereabouts and the first event of national importance he remembers is the celebration that marked the defeat of the Spanish Armada.) Yet his conservatism, and that of men like him, causes James I some unease. The king flinches when these quiet, respectable subjects allow the bells of their parish churches to ring in memory of Elizabeth's accession. And John Askew's wife? Let her share his piety and show compassion for the poor and sick that come begging at the Marsh Grange door. Let her order her household competently, entertain generously and educate her daughters, if not liberally, then after the best manner of her day. And her loyalties? She is a dozen years younger than her husband and only just remembers the old queen's passing and James Stuart's accession but, because she is a woman of the seventeenth century, she follows his lead. In any case, she likes to hear the bells ring out in celebration as her carriage takes her into Dalton on a dull November day.

October 1623: Margaret paused on the deep ledge of the landing window. Kneeling, she pressed her forehead against the glass and stared out, wrinkling her face with the effort of concentration. She stared hard past the yard and its outbuildings, beyond the field of cattle and the ragged line of trees, beyond the marsh that gave the house its name, to the shoreline and the sea. The grey brown of the sand gave way to the grey blue of sea and sky. She searched for phantom ships on the horizon and magical creatures in the sky. Only the seabirds shrieked. Satisfied with the boundary of her world she settled her attention on the comings and goings nearer at hand. Voices carried from the yard outside: orders given shortly and acknowledged with a grunt, a door slammed, cart wheels and horses' hooves rattled on cobbles. She caught the mingled smell of people and animals, of indoors and out. Her mother's clear tones and the squeals and giggles of her younger sister drifted up the stairwell. She heard her father's arrival and, abandoning her solitude, ran downstairs into the secure world of childhood and family prayers.

The child slips into her place in the hall with a swiftness born of habit. This is where she belongs. She takes comfort from the familiar. Her fingers trace the maze-like pattern on the carved armrest of the wooden settle. Almost unconsciously she notes the magical presence of the unicorn on its cushion. Her foot finds the crack in a flagstone worn by time. She looks round: at the quiet calm of her father's face, at the remoteness of her mother's, at the small sister now sucking her fingers baby fashion, at the indoor and outdoor servants of the Marsh Grange estate.

Her place in the world is something Margaret knows instinctively. She is a child of Marsh Grange, sheltered by the Elizabethan dignity of the house and by her father's wealth. She is the master's daughter who can move between hall and kitchen and be spoiled or scolded in both. Occasionally she glimpses the power and responsibility that go with John Askew's rank. She knows about the poor, the beggars and the vagrants, just as she knows about magic and witchcraft, but none of this knowing threatens her security. Marsh Grange is her fortress. Eventually she will make her first forays into the outside world from the safety of its walls.

The older Margaret smiles at the younger but remains captive in her own thoughts. She counts days and weeks and rehearses her body's symptoms. She loves her daughters but she lives in the shadow of difficult and sickly pregnancies that have ended in miscarriage, still birth or a child that lived but a few days. She is afraid. She reaches out to touch her children and prays that God will let her live but she knows he will not send her a lusty son to inherit her husband's land and his wealth.

There is love in the look John Askew sends her. He thinks he understands but he has too many worries. The harvest has been scant, one of the worst in his memory. Men are already comparing it with the hunger year at the end of old queen's reign. It will be a comfortless winter. If he is to buy corn dearly, he needs a good price for his animals. He doubts he'll get it. The whole north is hit by scarcity. There will be little enough money available to buy livestock. He prays that God will provide.

And the children? They sense the seriousness, but not its causes. Soon they fidget and shuffle their feet as children do, and the younger child tries to hide from the older in the folds of her mother's skirts, but their father looks down over the leather bound-bible he is opening and they become solemn again in an instant.

> And the people chode with Moses, and spake, saying... Why have ye thus brought the Congregation of the Lord into this wildernesse, that both we and our cattell should die there...Then Moses and Aaron went from the assembly unto the doore of the Tabernacle of the Congregation, fell upon their faces: and the glory of the Lord appeared unto them. And the Lord spake unto Moses, saying, Take the rod, and gather thou, and thy brother Aaron the Congregation together, and speake ye to the rocke before their eyes; and it shall give forth his water ...Then Moses lift up his hand, and with his rod he smote the rock twice, and the water came out abundantly: so the Congregation and their beasts dranke.

The famine of 1623 was God's will. The north of England went hungry. John Askew, educated, even scholarly man that he was, had no explanation. He did not know the causes of crop blight and cattle murrain. When his people were threatened with starvation he prayed. He gave alms to the poor but what good were alms when there was no bread to buy? Better to pray. God sent John Askew no miracles.

In the January and February of 1624 Furness buried its famine dead. The lightweight coffins of the very old and very young were carried to the churchyards and lowered into frozen ground that was difficult to break with a spade. Margaret, wife of John Askew, bore a stillborn son and mourned him and her own frailty. The old one of the marsh and shore died. The body wasn't found until the thaw. Some said it carried the stench of hell. Some said it was uncorrupted. They buried the corpse in unconsecrated ground outside the churchyard. Gifts and posies were placed on the unmarked grave until the grass grew again and the people stopped coming.

The year turned round: spring came. Seed could be bought, at a price. Another crop was planted. John Askew prayed again for a good harvest.

When I was five I knew where the gates of heaven were. They hung from the middle nail on the back wall of the old shop between the empty chairs and the broken hearts, just as at home the forks were always in the middle of the cutlery tray between the knives and the spoons. The old shop wasn't really a shop any more. It was where my uncles made wreaths: mossing up wire frames, chopping flower heads from stems and impaling them on rigid metal stalks to jab them into the waiting moss with deft, rapid movements. They talked endlessly. The chatter and the jokes were a comfortable background to the child sitting on the step searching for treasure in the debris. The air was full of the smell of decay, rotting leaves and stems and the sharper tang of florist's moss. Memory claims the scent of the flowers as chrysanthemums whatever the season. Once the last bloom was rammed home my Uncle John James would be attacked by a great heaving coughing fit and scuttle outside to indulge in a Woodbine away from Aunt Anna's eyes. He'd been in Burma for five years of the war but the cough was regarded as a family legacy. We knew the Jameses were 'creaking doors'. His sister Dolly spent the whole of my growing up in dying. My Uncle John Palmer would rummage around in the till and find me a shiny threepenny bit to go and choose sweets from the newsagents at the corner. Then he'd call through to the back kitchen for tea and two worlds would come together over thick china cups and hot brown liquid.

The women, my mother and her sisters, didn't really belong in the old shop world. Somehow they threatened its magic. The gates of heaven and the broken hearts became just flowers and moss and wire and the pounds, shillings and pence that made a living.

* * * * *

There followed a time that was neither wholly good nor wholly bad. God sent as many early springs as He did hard winters. Wool prices rose a little; then fell again. Cattle disease was still rife but most of the herd survived. Harvests were good enough to avert famine. Mewling infants survived in cottages where, even in good years, they didn't need another mouth to feed.

At Marsh Grange John Askew's wife bore no more children. She thanked God for the mercy that allowed her to watch over her daughters' growing up. She safeguarded the first letters written in a bold, round, childlike hand and mounted the samplers on which they learned to stitch. She sang the songs of her own childhood and later taught her daughters to pick out their melodies. Teaching them part songs she shared their wonder at notes that seemed to meet in mid-air. She heard Margaret recite her catechism and listened patiently as her younger sister spelt out the stories of Noah's Flood or David and Goliath.

Margaret learned the religion of her parents. It represented habit and comfort and it made few demands on the child for it was part of the pattern of her days. Household prayers were about her own father's gathering of his people together. They were about family and belonging and looking after and taking care of. They were a way of giving the day back to God and saying thank you. It was a time to ask for God's mercy and forgiveness. It was a time to listen to the magical, mysterious stories of Scripture.

To the child churchgoing was at once the same and different. It held the excitement of the carriage ride, the stomach-churning up and down of the hill through Ireleth, the more sedate climb to the church on top of Dalton's hill, the meetings with friends and neighbours, the chatter and the noise and finally the solemnity.

Medieval masons hewed the stone for Dalton church. They were creating the setting for a way of worship they expected to last forever. Now, a century of reformation later, the most dramatic links with the

Catholic past have gone. The great Rood, flanked by the figures of the Virgin Mary and John the Baptist, no longer hangs above the chancel arch. Yet, the musty smells of incense and candle smoke cling to the fabric and much of the imagery has been left to fade in God's good time. The three Marys, St. Barbara and St. Nicholas still look down from the windows. Sunlight filters through stained glass; specks of coloured light play in the shadows. The wall paintings may need skilled restoration to bring their stories back to life but they have not been hidden by whitewash. Near the north door stands St. Christopher, the Christ Child on his shoulders, his staff plunged into water once so real that fish swam around in it. The seven deadly sins emerge from a tree with roots guarded by the demons of childhood nightmares. Christ of the Trades is surrounded by craftsmen's tools: here are the reaper's scythe, the shoemaker's awl, the weaver's shuttle. For Margaret as a child, the church was an enclosed world. If she stood on tiptoe and peered over the top of the box pew she found the stuff of which dreams and stories are made. As a young woman she already felt stifled by the child's world. She was beginning to understand that the same fabric that sheltered the child could suffocate the adult. She didn't try to explain her malaise and like us all she followed custom and habit. The five-year-old Margaret had bidden St. Christopher farewell with a noisy enthusiasm that had to be shushed by her mother; the fifteen-year-old offered him a silent, grudging and somewhat embarrassed goodbye.

The old images manage a kind of coexistence with the new theology. The priest offers his congregation communion in two kinds and they accept both bread and wine. The liturgy he uses emphasises the symbolic nature of the ceremony. But does it matter as long as God protects the weak and the industrious and punishes the sinner? The saints no longer intercede between God and man but if they look down beneficently from walls and windows, who is going to complain? Not this rural congregation, nor their ill-trained priest trying to manage a parish of forty-eight square miles and twenty villages, nor even the bishop in distant Carlisle. At least, not yet.

From the chancel arch the priest intones the collect for grace:

> O Lord our heavenly Father, almighty and
> everlasting God which hath safely brought us
> to the beginning of this day, defend us in the
> same with thy mighty power, and grant that
> this day we fall into no sinne, neither run into
> any kind of danger, but that all our doings
> may be ordered by thy governance to doe
> that which is righteous in thy light, through
> Jesus Christ our Lord. Amen.

The congregation echoes the 'amen'. God is worshipped in the English of Elizabeth's prayer book. The new liturgy has served three generations. It is beginning to carry the authority of tradition. The ritual is still there in the relationship between priest and people. There is poetry in the rhythms and cadences of the language. For some it is enough that this church is English and Protestant, not Roman and Catholic. For others it will never be more than a stepping stone to a truly reformed religion.

The people pray:

> The Father which in heaven art, and maketh
> us all one brotherhood: To call upon thee
> with one heart, Our heavenly Father and our
> God: Grant wee pray not with lippes alone.
> But with the hearts deepesigh and grone

An Essex new town at the end of the 1950s. It was a place just beginning. There were roads without houses and houses without roads. There was land bought for development but as yet undeveloped where children raced bicycles over long summer holidays and stole too many green apples, struggling home bloated and ill. Streets smelt of fresh tar and houses of plaster and paint. Everything had a kind of fresh scrubbed, almost temporary, air. Woolworths was a mobile shop that arrived on Saturdays and vanished again. There was a church made of concrete and glass with the kind of floor on which chairs screeched discordantly. A vicar and a Church Army captain worked to build community in a place without continuity. God was welcome for a while but then the secular world exerted its pull with Mecca dances, the bingo hall and the pub, all built of the same concrete and glass as the church but with brighter lights and louder music.

* * * * *

> I was brought up and lived with my Father,
> until I was between Seventeen and Eighteen
> Years of Age and then I was married …

The year is 1630. Charles I has been king for five years. His queen, Henrietta Maria, has just born the son who will become Charles II. Margaret Askew is sixteen. She lives in the sunshine of her own springtime. She dances on the edge of the adult world. With her parents, she exchanges neighbourhood visits and learns the rules by which hospitality is given and received. She rides to Conishead beyond Ulverston to celebrate the feast of Easter. The Doddings are Puritan in politics and religion but not yet so Puritan that they will have no laughter or dancing in their lives. John Askew shares his host's disquiet at the policies being pursued in church and state by Charles Stuart, his French Catholic wife and his Bishop of London, William Laud, whose Anglicanism seems more Catholic than Protestant. He will talk the visit away with men of his own persuasion. But he notices how anticipation and excitement make his daughter glow. And Margaret knows she looks well in her new wool gown although she is young enough and worldly enough to regret the absence of silk to rustle. She takes full pleasure in the moment and joins the young Doddings and the Kirkbys of Ireleth in their chatter and music and laughter. Her mother looks on. The older woman knows the match-making must start soon. Her eye catches that of young Miles Dodding, all gangling limbs and amiable grin. She has known him since he was in short coats but she senses he is not for her daughter, nor these other unfinished youths with their ready bellows of amusement or anger.

Margaret understands that the interlude, which is her life now, must end in marriage. She hears of matches made by other daughters and contracts drawn up by other fathers. She knows Marsh Grange is part of her portion and her father wants the future of his land secured as much as he does that of his daughter. She watches serving maid handfasted to stable lad on the Marsh Grange estate. She's too young and too gently bred to fully understand the ribaldry that accompanies the ceremony but she can connect it with the stirrings of her own body. Romance and adventure people her dreams although the objects of her desire make but a brief sojourn there. For a night she takes flight with a gallant captain newly returned from deeds of heroism in distant lands. For a day she sighs after the ascetic profile a young man in a soutane back, they said, from the continent, where he was training for the Catholic priesthood.

Margaret's mother sees her own adult life beginning again in that of her daughter. She cannot talk to her about the marriage bed and the child-bed, about pleasure and fear. She does not want to talk about home leaving and aloneness and loneliness. Instead she teaches her daughter domestic economy. Margaret follows her mother from linen closet to storeroom to dairy. She learns about household accounts and the management of servants. She is shown how to prepare possets and care for the sick. She stitches shifts, hems linen and works fine embroidery. She waits.

The photographs were in the sideboard drawer with the embroidered tablecloths and the place mats decorated with pictures of old London. They were packed away in a chocolate box: on its lid a muslin-clad woman sheltered under a parasol. Mum used to get them out to dream over them under pretence of tidying up. Wartime brides preserved in sepia, lips and cheeks tastefully tinted by the photographer. They hoarded coupons for the frocks, the skirts as full as rationing allowed. The men wore khaki or naval blue. There was a shiny black and white print of me on a tricycle and one of my brother sitting in his pram looking like a cherub with his mass of blond curls. Family life as it might have been. Later I found a likeness of my grandmother, sitting upright on a kitchen chair outside a house I barely remember, hair drawn severely back in a bun, eyes staring into the middle distance, work worn hands resting on her aproned lap. Her mouth was compressed. There was no concessionary smile for the occasion. She used to sit like that in the shop doorway calling, 'Daffs, lovely daffs!' She could shout, could my grandmother. The aunts were never too keen on the street-market tones she brought to their post-war prosperity. Did they expect polite whispers from a woman who had raised seven children on the profits of selling flowers to the poor? Mostly it was funeral flowers. All she read was the *South London Press*, from cover to cover, starting with the deaths. There was no photograph of her mother, my great-grandmother Emma, who did the unforgivable and abandoned her child. I wish I knew if that was tragedy or adventure.

John Askew gives his elder daughter a Bible. She runs her hand over the tracery of the leather cover. The thick volume is printed in heavy gothic type. Much later someone will add a handwritten note on the flyleaf explaining that the translation is the work of Miles Coverdale, Anthony Gilby and other Englishmen with less well-known names, although the Scot John Knox is there too. Margaret does not need to be told that the translators are Protestant divines who had cause to fear the fires of Catholic Mary's reign and fled to Calvin's Geneva. The Bible she holds has survived as a monument to their faith and scholarship. It is uncompromisingly English and Protestant. The printer has added a preface in verse:

Here is the Spring where waters flow,
To quench our heart of sinne:
Here is the Tree where trueth doth grow,
To leade our lives therein:

Later Margaret would be less accepting of the simplicity of the verse maker's theology. By then the Bible would be well thumbed. She would have read far more than the stories that coloured her childhood. Now the book feels like a blessing and a leave-taking but she has nowhere to go.

Once I waited too, impatient with the on-the-brink-of-life anticipation of young womanhood, hoping to conquer…what? A kingdom? Or its king?

* * * * *

…I was married unto Thomas Fell of Swarthmoor, who was a Barrister-at-Law of Gray's Inn.

Thomas Fell, gentleman farmer, landowner, man of law, later granted a small place in history and a more prominent one in Quaker mythology. Who was he, this man who was to marry Margaret Askew and live with her for twenty-six years?

Thomas Fell received his legal training at Grays Inn. It was a hotbed of radicalism, not just political opposition to the Stuart monarchy, but religious nonconformity too. England's adoption of the Protestantism of the continental reformers had been a very cautious affair. The Anglicanism put on to the statute book by Elizabeth and endorsed by James I left the English Church as far from Geneva as it was from Rome. Those who called themselves Puritans wanted to purify the Anglican establishment of the last vestiges of what they regarded as Catholic ritual and to remove the emphasis on liturgy in favour of one on preaching. The basis of their faith was the Bible, expounded by the minister. It was to Calvin's Geneva that they owed theological allegiance, holding to a doctrine of predestination, and striving to assure themselves of their own salvation by the practice of personal devotion and communal piety. Much of their time and money was spent on the maintenance of Puritan lectureships outside the framework of the Anglican Church. They would have sermons despite the opposition of the monarch and the clerical establishment.

If Thomas was not a Puritan when he left Furness for London, the years in the capital made him one. The Grays Inn lawyers hired their own 'godly preaching ministers'; Thomas's soul was well taught while he kept his terms and learned his trade. The lawyers had no taste for what they saw happening within the established church, where Charles Stuart seemed to be intent on reviving Catholic practice if not Catholic theology.

In January 1631 William Laud, Bishop of London, confidant of Charles I, consecrated the church of St Catherine Cree, built to grace the city, its vast nave divided by elegant colonnades, its altar richly adorned. The Puritan city, far from being pleased, shuddered. Bishop Laud arrived to conduct the ceremony clothed in all the over-dressed pomposity of office. The elaborate consecration ritual was said to be of his own devising, an unpleasant taste of things to come. When Laud was tried for treason in 1645 his enemies claimed he had used 'divers curses' in the consecration of Cree church. St Catherine's railed altar, its ornately robed priest bowing at the name of Jesus and its scent of incense and candles, angered and alarmed Puritans who wanted the Protestant Reformation of the church completed, not this return to Roman ways. Laud's new church pro-vided a backdrop for ritual. What his opponents wanted was a church in which the pulpit loomed larger than the altar. They had no taste for Laud's stage set.

Oxford in the late '60s. An hour to pass between the Bodleian and college dinner. Choral evensong in Magdalen chapel. An academic exercise in aesthetics set to the music of Byrd or Tallis. The background was pure gothic splendour and the singing magnificent. Music and poetry walked hand in hand, but where was God?

Cree church survived its Puritan opponents, the Great Fire and the Blitz. It still stands at the Aldgate end of Leadenhall Street although, today, sandwiched between office blocks, it looks less imposing. The massive towers of twentieth-century business have dwarfed Laud's Anglican landmark: the London Association of Underwriters and Swiss Reinsurance dominate the modern Leadenhall Street. A notice board claims St Catherine's as the 'guild church of industry, finance and commerce'. Perhaps City gods were ever the same.

Thomas Fell turned his back on St Catherine Cree. He could not seek God through ritual and symbol. 'Labour after a right understanding of the true nature of Christianity and the meaning of the Gospel', wrote the Puritan preacher Richard Baxter. Thomas Fell had begun to labour after his own kind of truth. The labour shaped his political outlook. If the established church were to be further reformed those reforms would have to be sanctioned by the King as 'supreme governor' of the church. Charles I wanted reformation no more than he wanted discussion. He attempted to ban controversial sermons but all he did was to drive the Puritans behind closed doors. The sermons were still preached and religious discontent hardened political opposition to the monarchy.

The Grays Inn lawyers had no more liking for Charles' increasingly autocratic behaviour towards parliament and subjects than they did for his religion. It was difficult to oppose a monarchy that claimed to rest on divine right. Who are men to gainsay what God has instituted? But England had to be protected from bad government so the lawyers in parliament had revived the medieval practice of impeachment, or trial by parliament, to rid the king of 'evil councillors'. The myth of the separate guilt of the crown's servants allowed the opponents of the monarchy to attack unpopular ministers while assuming the king's holy innocence, almost until the moment of crisis that brought Charles Stuart to the scaffold in 1649.

The parliaments of the 1620s thought that they could control the King. Parliament saw itself as protector of the 'liberties' of Englishmen. It's not a word that translates easily into our terms. It had nothing to do with democratic rights and freedoms. Early Stuart parliaments limited themselves to the protection of the rights and privileges of the governing class, the landowning gentry and nobility, a mere two per cent of the population. Parliament's apparent moment of glory came in 1629. Charles I's need for money was so great that he gave his assent to the Petition of Right drawn up by his House of Commons. He yielded his right to collect taxation without parliamentary consent, his right to arbitrary arrest of his subjects and to the arbitrary billeting of troops. Parliament was sovereign; but the king then dissolved parliament. The lawyers must have spent hours debating the actual balance of power at this point. But the very nature of monarchy was to give the king the advantage. Parliament remained dissolved and the King ruled.

There was little the opposition could do except talk their displeasure, a situation which did not stop Thomas Fell nursing political ambition. He wanted his share of the offices and powers that went with wealth and land, not that he was particularly wealthy as yet but his estate provided a modestly comfortable starting point for further acquisition. He was an astute lawyer too; his talents demanded work and reward. For now Thomas's life was elsewhere. As summer's heat added to the stench of the capital and rumours of plague spread he left London for the north. He went home to his estate of Swarthmoor, to land inherited from his father, to fulfil the role that tradition demanded of him.

The families at Conishead, Plumpton, Kirkby Ireleth and Marsh Grange welcomed Thomas Fell's return. They wanted to see Swarthmoor occupied and its owner settled. Social order was maintained in the manor houses just as it was in the churches. In the fullness of time Thomas met John Askew's elder daughter. Did he love her at first sight? It happened even then.

> The first Lord's day being Oct 6 my eye fixed
> with love upon a Mayd and hers upon me
> who afterwards proved my wife,

wrote Ralph Josselin, Puritan minister and diarist, of his first meeting with Jane. By December he had refused a Norfolk living for the sake of staying close to her and within a year they had settled into the Earl's Colne rectory that was to be their home for forty-three years.

'He was a tender loving husband to me', wrote Margaret long after Thomas's death. The beginning she kept to herself.

In 1631 Thomas Fell was thirty-three: Margaret was almost seventeen. He was just back from London: she had only been as far as Lancaster. He had the assurance that goes with experience and independence: she was John Askew's daughter. Something within her responded to the energy and ambition she sensed in Thomas although she could not name it. He fell captive to her youth. He had Swarthmoor, worth £150 per year, and she had a marriage portion of £3000 that included Marsh Grange. The land mattered.

Margaret recognised the expectations of her family and her own needs. Like Juliet, before the advent of Romeo, she could promise her mother that she would 'look to like, if looking liking move'. No Romeo appeared. She continued to look and to like. Thomas wakened her mind: her body was content to follow. His admiration flattered her and his kindness often surprised her. When she agreed to become his wife his grave happiness overwhelmed her. She had made her decision and she allowed herself to be carried along by the elation that accompanied its making. Margaret and Thomas made the mutual promises that were their private contract. They were betrothed. To their friends they became a couple. Thomas and John Askew drew up the formal, public marriage contract. They followed the custom of their day with love and concern. Margaret would be legally bound but she would be legally protected too. And at length she rode across the sands to Lancaster to choose silk for her wedding gown.

In 1632 Margaret Askew and Thomas Fell married. We do not know when. So let us make it the springtime when the first primroses were in full bloom close to the church walls. Nor do we know where. Let us have her travel to Ulverston for the ceremony that will mark the start of her new life. Archbishop Bancroft's canons of 1604 are still in force and say only that a marriage should be solemnised in the parish of one of the parties. St. Mary's, Ulverston, is more imposing than Dalton church and will more easily accommodate the company gathered to wish the couple well. Besides Thomas wishes to share his happiness and feast his friends royally.

Margaret and Thomas marry in an Anglican church that will soon be reshaped by William Laud as Archbishop of Canterbury. Oddly the established church had no legal monopoly of marriage. They could have been handfasted or exchanged spousals (private vows) at Marsh Grange or Swarthmoor as long as they had witnesses. They would have been just as married in the eyes of the world. But they follow custom as their rank demands, and they ask God's blessing on their union as their hearts demand. Standing before priest and altar Margaret finds it hard to quiet the whirl in her mind. She steps aside from her dressed up, grown up self and is overawed by the importance of the occasion. The words of the homily on matrimony flow over her: 'to the intent that man and woman should live lawfully in a perpetual friendship'. Phrases repeat in her head. How long is perpetual? She is oppressed by the enormity of words and by the depth of feelings. 'Procreation', 'worship', 'body', 'perpetual', 'forever'; what have they to do with her? She tries to concentrate. The pious woman stills the uncomprehending child. Her groom stands uneasily in this Anglican setting, although Laud's influence has not yet spread this far north and St. Mary's is, in truth, much as it was when Thomas was a child. Now he determinedly keeps his attention on the rise and fall of the silk of his bride's gown and away from the brocade of the priestly vestments. For once his heart and his increasingly Puritan conscience dictate the same thing. The groom looks fondly on the bride and she on him. Thomas Fell takes Margaret Askew to be his wedded wife and she takes him to be her wedded husband. They exchange rings and the service proceeds. Any hesitation or clumsiness is attributed to emotion or nervousness, as is only proper at a wedding. Their friends sigh, blink back fugitive tears of sentiment and smile. They are free to leave the constraining walls of sombre St. Mary's for sunlight and celebration. With lighter hearts bride and groom follow tradition and present their guests with gloves as a keepsake of the occasion.

In another time and another world, where customs had changed, and the church had again lost whatever monopoly it might have established over marriage, another couple exchanged vows, or promises, or something in the dusty office of a New Zealand registrar. At ten to twelve on a hot December morning as the temperature passed ninety degrees, we were hurtled towards wedded bliss by an official determined to lunch at noon: a civil ceremony conducted in the flat vowels of 'God's own country'. Even then we weren't sure what had been said. More than half a lifetime later the beginning is still recorded in the stark legal black and white of a marriage certificate and a badly focused photograph of a couple caught standing awkwardly under a palm tree in the harsh glare of a foreign sun. We lunched, substantially but without elegance, among beer drinking businessmen in the upstairs room of the local pub and caught the limited express to Wellington. A curious twentieth-century rite of passage that ended with a ride on a cowboy train and a flight to Australia. We spent two weeks in Queensland's unchanging humidity, growing torpid and dull among strangers in an alien city. The sudden tropical rain was a liberation. Walking a metalled road, thick red mud splattered our legs. But like the pineapple fields and the eucalyptus trees and the scrawny patches of grass in gardens I awoke and worshipped rain, the spirit of English summers.

* * * * *

1633: Margaret Askew has become Margaret Fell. She has left Marsh Grange for Swarthmoor. This house with its unfamiliar rooms is almost the twin of her former home. She catches herself fingering the tapestry cushions of a window seat searching for half-remembered darns and bare patches. She knows there is no retreating into childhood and struggles with the burden of her new role. Nobody had prepared her for the loneliness of marriage. She must learn to live in Thomas's world, with his people. Somehow it is much easier to strive to be Swarthmoor's mistress than Thomas's wife. She listens to the maidservants giggling together and is at once excluded and embarrassed. Tears prick her eyelids. She keeps them there by a huge effort of will and stretches to her full, she hopes authoritative, height. It is time she visited kitchen and dairy. Her household must know it is managed.

Thomas treats her with an unvarying kindness she sometimes misunderstands. She interprets it as lack of concern or, worse, lack of interest. Now she stabs her needle uneasily at the sleeve of a shirt and follows his movements with her eyes as he settles himself in the wooden chair at the other end of the great bay window. Soon he will ask about her day. She doesn't know what answers to give. She tries roles in her mind. Was she the pious, studious woman who read her Bible or the charitable chatelaine who gave alms to beggars at her door? Was she the careful mistress who took stock of her linen cupboard or the young wife who returned the bridal calls of her neighbours? She plays the roles well enough but sometimes she wants to make her bid for freedom or curl up like a child and cry for home. She does not know what Thomas expects of her. She does not know how to go about the day-to-day business of living with this man. They manage a diffident, stilted communication until the candles start to gutter and it is time to retire. She watches him again now as he rises to his feet and pauses to look at the dying embers of the fire. Their eyes meet. She reddens and smiles and reddens again. Unable to tell what he wants of her or she of him, she tries to reconcile her instincts and her upbringing. She cannot talk about her body's yearnings to anybody, least of all to the worldly, urbane man facing her now. She does not know if she communicates shyness, naiveté, or pleasure born of instinct, for she can no more separate those qualities than she can name them to herself. Later the salt tang of sweat on his back tells her that she is his.

It's a knowledge that brings no security. Margaret senses the power and the hint of ruthlessness behind Thomas's benevolence. She is conscious of his strength but she does not yet know her own. For now he dominates her and she cannot break the pattern. Nor is she sure that she wants to. Still a stranger in his world, she does not understand his deep need of her.

The Fells ride to Plumpton Hall on the other side of Ulverston. John Sawrey has bidden them to dine. The sight of the house on the flat land fronting beach and sea leaves Margaret with an overwhelming longing for Marsh Grange. Thomas spends half a day locked in political discussion with Sawrey, a man whose Puritanism in politics and religion is more severe than his own. They watch national events closely, these men of the north. William Laud still has the king's confidence: since August he has had the see of Canterbury as well. Charles Stuart has yet to summon Parliament. Soon he will need money. The purses of Fell and Sawrey are fat enough to be taxed. They hold fast to their right to give their assent to any royal demand for subsidy but can only do so if the king calls Parliament. Others arrive to share their counsels. Thomas Birch of Birch is one of these. Margaret does not like these friends of Thomas. Their intensity frightens her. Her discomfort becomes physical when Birch smothers her with his polished civilities. She is almost glad to be left to the attentions of their wives, the bride among matrons, a part she suspects she plays clumsily.

Strangers, we learnt how to live together in a strange land. We had the public, professional and social world we shared. We needed one another to walk with in this alien landscape. We stayed close to those who saw themselves as expatriates. Memory acts as a bond even if the only common factors are wet days at the seaside and the layer of ice on the free school milk of childhood.

We tried to create a private world. We arranged wedding presents, lovingly packed and crated twelve thousand miles away, in houses we never completely furnished. We fenced and sparred and loved. We learnt to be a couple. I conceived your child. I thought we would put down roots. Have we?

* * * * *

Margaret knows she is with child. Pride and despair engulf her by turns. She is a woman of her own time knowing no security in pregnancy and childbirth. She fights fear and nausea with equal determination, able to do nothing but look on as her womb swells, her breasts grow tender and her ankles puffy. It is almost as if the experience is happening to someone else. Yet she must slow down to the child's pace. Her life is increasingly confined, now that she cannot ride out on visits. Thomas sits with his ledgers and law books, distanced by her fecundity. Fatherhood gives weight to ambition. His wife must rest content with stitching swaddling clothes and take what comfort she can from her Bible. She finds other women can be less than comforting. Eve brought forth her sons with no greater sorrow than every Mary, Jane or Elizabeth of Margaret's acquaintance. With each passing month, with each kindly-meant child-bed tale that is forced on her, her uncertainty grows. Margaret thinks of her mother. She remembers the years when the older woman seemed to retreat into her own unhappiness. All she can do now is wait, and the waiting hurts.

In the weeks before her eldest daughter's birth she lives with fear on two levels. There are crazed irrational moments when she woke in panic, her breasts aching and her womb cramped, the child momentarily still within her so that she has no assurance of its survival. At such times she is convinced that no woman has suffered like this before and that the end can only be death or, worse, deformity. She cannot give Thomas an imperfect child. By day realism takes over but it is a realism which leaves her acutely aware of her own vulnerability. She understands the risks she is taking with her body and her life and, because she understands, she knows real fear.

It was not knowledge she could share with a man who offered her his heartfelt but calm concern. Margaret was alone. Her powerlessness was that of all the women of her generation. She could but pray.

In search of Margaret Fell

In the Essex village of Earls Colne, Ralph Josselin wrote of his Jane that she was 'oppressed with feares that she should not doe well on this child'. Poor Jane Josselin, so often in the pages of her husband's diary she 'breedeth with difficultie'. He could not understand the full extent of her fear but he had 'prayd with confidence of good successe to her'. God answered Ralph's prayers and the next day Jane was safely delivered of their third child.

In Puritan New England Anne Bradstreet tried to explain to Simon

> How soon, my Dear, death may my steps attend,
> How soon't may be thy lot to lose thy friend,
> We both are ignorant, yet love bids me
> These farewell lines to recommend to thee,

Anne Bradstreet wrote in rhyme but this was no sentimental verse making. As a young woman Anne had crossed a hostile Atlantic on John Winthrop's flagship the *Arbella*. She knew about the hardship and suffering of the raw, new world of a Massachusetts which was not yet the Puritan 'city upon a hill' of Winthrop's imagination. Her own, and her world's, attitude to motherhood carried its toll of emotional and physical pain. Anne Bradstreet had been married five years before she conceived her first child, five long years imagining herself barren. She was barely twenty-one when her eldest son was born: those years of uncertainty toughened her. Now she urged Simon to:

> Look to my little babes my dear remains.
> And if thou love thy self, or loved'st me
> These O protect from step Dames injury.

Did he ever really accept what she was telling him? More likely, he glimpsed the despair and pushed the poem to the back of a drawer. Simon and Anne Bradstreet brought up eight children in the new colony. Anne lived to record the deaths of their infant grandchildren.

Anne Clifford, alone on her Yorkshire estate, writing her journal with hands stiffened and blotched by age, recorded the death of her granddaughter, 'being then in labour of her first Childe which was a Sonne of whom she could not be delivered, for the Childe was dead within a few houres before her own death.' Anne Clifford remembered her own fears. She remembered her joy in her daughters and her grief for the three sons who had died in infancy. Three pregnancies in as many years had ended in mourning. Now, in her old age, she knew just how frail the links between generations were.

Margaret's child was born as the year turned. Swarthmoor's women came to help her at the birthing. It was their bonding with her and hers with the place. They treated her with the rough kindness of those who have no time for self-indulgence. She had expected pain but the ferocity with which her daughter entered the world showed her the limits of her physical self. She was torn and bleeding and exhausted. Yet she was healthy and young and she would heal. She knew complete tenderness and love for the wrinkled infant, rejoicing in her daughter's perfection when she presented her to Thomas. At last she slept, secure in her own belonging.

In a world which had institutionalised birth and death, a woman in labour crossed the helter-skelter pass of a New Zealand mountain to the vastness of a Dunedin teaching hospital. They wheeled her through corridors that were marvels of tiled sterility. Her son was delivered by a medical student logging births for his finals, a fledgling authority on women's bodies. There was still the wonder of new-born perfection and the endless fascination of tiny hands and feet. There was still the surfeit of emotion and the physical exhaustion. Although here, there was too much clinical cleanliness and brusque professionalism for death to catch you unaware. Bonding between mother and child was difficult in this so orderly institution, but a kind of female comradeship grew from commonly suffered indignities. There are other memories too of a country that was foreign and strange. The deep-throated laughter of a Maori welcome given to a small olive-skinned Polynesian. The high country farmer's wife, released from the loneliness of a sheep station up Central, who treated the experience of the hospital ward as an extension of schooldays and dormitory japes. And through all this there is still the raw-eyed stoicism of a luckless adolescent, trapped in this married women's world, while the grown-ups signed adoption papers for the child this society wouldn't allow her to love. Not then. Not in 1974.

Rite of passage. I took my child back to a rented house on the edge of a one-street Otago town, a house which was always more landing stage than home, and thought about the twelve thousand miles that separated this new world from the old, while I watched the winter sun sink behind the snow-capped Kakanui mountains.

Margaret lay propped against her pillows peering at the grey sky beyond her window. She was a willing prisoner in a female world. She nursed the child and was nursed and fussed over in her turn. Thomas gave thanks for her safe delivery, admired his first born distantly and withdrew. Margaret Askew arrived on a birth visit with her younger daughter. The older woman enjoyed but fragile health. She thanked God that her blood ran in the veins of this infant. The younger seemed overawed by Margaret's confinement to this room and this bed. Her eyes flickered uneasily over her sister's full breasts and the small swaddled bundle that was her niece. Eventually she chattered, easily enough, of Dalton news but it was the social chatter of a stranger. Margaret understood that she had left the world of Marsh Grange forever. The child bound her to Swarthmoor in a way that Thomas did not.

The infant was baptised Margaret for her mother and her grand-mother. Thomas invited the priest to Swarthmoor to name his small daughter and to bid her welcome to church and community. The welcome was important to Margaret. It was one of the threads that would weave her child's sense of identity. She wasn't sure about the other meanings of the ceremony. She wanted her daughter to belong: to have her own people, her own church and her own God. Love would not let her dwell on the image of a heaven that excluded the souls of unbaptised babes, anymore than it would let her contemplate the death of the child she wanted to protect so fiercely.

Rain spattered the window. Margaret heard the rush of the wind and, feeling a sudden surge of energy, wanted to run into the outside world. Yet custom dictated that she sit out the terms of her confinement. She kept to her bed and her room for a full three weeks. At last she had the freedom of the hall. She stood uncomfortably on untried muscles and dressed with the help of her maid. In those weeks when custom forbade her to go abroad she walked from room to room, owning the fabric of the house and its carved wooden furniture, learning its moods and preparing to take charge. She needed to come to terms with a new self who wanted to lay her own claim to Swarthmoor.

First she must declare her own readiness to return to the world after the solitude of her confinement. She goes to St. Mary's to be churched. The churching of women is no longer a service of purification despite Archbishop Laud's demand that they come veiled to the altar. It has become a thanksgiving and a rite of passage. Margaret gives thanks for her own safety and that of her daughter. Her heart gives its own meaning to the ritual of priest and prayerbook. She has survived her moment of greatest vulnerability and she rejoices. She prays that her beautiful daughter will grow strong and loving. With her eyes on the thin beams of sunlight filtering through the stained glass of the east window, she repeats the words of the psalm:

> I will lift up mine eyes unto the hills,
> From whence cometh my help.
> My help cometh from the Lord,
> Which made heaven and earth.

She does not doubt that the psalmist's hills and hers are the same, made green by the same rain, hidden by the same mists. The bounds of her love extend to the country around her.

The birth marked another stage in her relationship with Thomas. Later when she lay beside him, her body curved to accommodate the spread of his limbs, she thought of him not as her husband but her daughter's father. She pictured his pride in the woman this babe would become.

In the years that followed, motherhood engulfed Margaret. She was a 'childing' woman: either 'big bellied' or newly confined. Young Margaret was born in 1633, Bridget in 1635, Isobel in 1637 and George in 1638. Her life took on its own rhythm: conception, pregnancy, birth, baptism, churching and conception again. Within five years she bore four children. Her babies were taken from swaddling bands and coated; they were nursed and weaned. First steps and first words were wondered at and delighted in. Swarthmoor was Margaret's world. She created her own magic. Later she lost touch with the busyness. All that remained were images that came fleetingly, one after another: the look of complete bafflement as an infant, lurching from chair to settle, fell bottom first; her children's heads sighted in a meadow full of June flowers, the older children's wonder at the beauty of the newest baby.

There was the magic of mid-winter. She wanted her children to marvel at the dark mystery of a candle-lit church on Christmas Eve. She needed to share the expectancy of a world waiting for the birth of the Christ Child in its own dark days. It was the point at which the ritual and order of the church year met her need for faith and hope. It was the point at which she felt most connected to past and future. Distantly she heard the words of a carol, already two hundred years old.

> Ne had the apple taken been, the apple taken been
> Ne had never our lady a-been heavene queen.

As she told her children the story of the nativity, she heard it again for the first time in their rapt attention. For the magic of the story creates itself anew at each retelling.

> And Joseph also went up from Galilee, out of
> the citie called Nazareth, into Judaea, unto
> the citie of David, which is called Bethlehem;

(because he was of the house and lineage of David) to be taxed with Mary that was given him to wife, which was with child. And so it was, that, while they were there, the days were accomplished that she should be delivered. And she brought forth her first begotten Sonne, and wrapped him in swaddling clothes, and laid him in a cratch; because there was no room for them in the Inne.

So the Christmas story was told and is told in parish churches and cathedrals. And the words and the music continue to hold their power. There was a year when the story was brought to life in the enchanted space of a theatre lit by the faint glow of braziers. A spell-bound child rested his head on my pregnant belly. Below us Christ was born as a bundle of swaddling bands. God appeared on a fork lift truck, and the wondering shepherds were droll, but the spell did not break and we were awe-struck anew by the power of the narrative.

Swarthmoor is the hub of Margaret's world. She has lost touch with the memories that connect her with Marsh Grange and Dalton. She visits at less and less frequent intervals. The family bonds of child-hood are tightened only by celebration or mourning. She rides across the peninsula with Thomas to celebrate her sister's marriage to the attorney Matthew Richardson. The two young women walk together in the Marsh Grange garden. They are alike to look at, the same curve of the hairline and set of the chin. The child-bearing full-ness of the older sister's figure makes the younger look almost ethe-real. There is something unreal about the young bride's determined gaiety and almost brittle laughter. Margaret feels distanced by it. She cannot talk about her own experience of marriage and becomes suddenly aware that her own happiness has grown from her sense of belonging; to Thomas, to Swarthmoor, to her children. The two women reach the end of the box hedge and turn almost at the same moment. Their eyes meet for a second and the distress behind the younger woman's smile shows. The contact isn't long enough to be a

In search of Margaret Fell

plea for help: the hurt is hardly allowed to surface before it is veiled. Margaret feels at once threatened and inadequate and prays this marriage will grow in love and not cause pain. She is suddenly beset by fears that her own wholeness might be undermined by the other woman's suffering. Her thoughts are interrupted by a renewed flow of inconsequential chatter. The sisters return to the house without allowing their eyes to meet again.

John Askew's second daughter was well dowered. Matthew Richardson signed the marriage contract readily enough. Perhaps he thought he could protect his bride from her own fragility. Perhaps he loved her for it.

Margaret continued to pray for them, or tried to pray. She did not visit. When she next entered the house on Duddon Sands her father was dying. John Askew knew his time had come. The good steward ordered his affairs, entrusted Marsh Grange to the care of his sons-in-law and relinquished his hold on life. His widow did not long survive him. The physical frailty that had been hers for life didn't allow her the strength to grieve. She slipped out of this world in her husband's shadow, deeply mourned but scarcely missed. Margaret's children were their link with the future. It mattered that in this generation there was a son to inherit. Margaret prayed at the grave-side. She thanked God that she had broken her mother's cycle of miscarriage and still birth. There were four children at Swarthmoor.

> The Lord is the portion of mine inheritance
> and of my cup: Thou shalt maintaine my lot.
>
> The lines are fallen unto me in pleasant
> places; yea, I have a faire heritage.

She would not long mourn her pious parents, whose lives had run their course. She refused to doubt that a merciful God would open heaven's gate for John Askew and his gentle wife. Her inheritance was her father's sense of stewardship. She would safeguard his grandchildren and their estate. That moment in Dalton churchyard marked her conscious acceptance of the responsibility she felt towards her family. She both recognised the path that was hers for now and knew she had the strength to walk it. She looked across at the grief-stricken face of her younger sister. She could not meet the wildness of despair in the other woman's eyes, sensing pain that went beyond grief and seemed to threaten her own resolve. She did not trust her own reactions in the face of unreason, derangement, or madness. She knew not what. Nor did she know if she could help. Matthew Richardson took his wife's arm and led her towards the waiting carriage. Four years married and no child yet: Margaret guessed her own obvious fertility offered no comfort. She had found her excuse and her Achilles heel. Quickly she prayed that sickness of the mind was not to be the lot of her children and as quickly regretted the impulse that had prompted the prayer. She returned to Swarthmoor aware of having failed but powerless to do otherwise.

Death tests our compassion for the living as much as it does our faith in God. How do we sympathise properly with those who react differently to us? I let my mother down when my father died but he wasn't just the man who bore cancer bravely. He was a man who hated to mend things or park cars in tight places. He was a man who liked pub company and malt whiskey. He was a man who stood for hours, calmly puffing on his pipe, while my sons watched trains or went endlessly up and down slides. He was a man... Death should not rob us of our humanity. Much later I listened to another woman recounting memories and fragments of memories and glimpsed the emptiness of widowhood.

> Looking down into my father's
> dead face
> for the last time
> my mother said
> without tears, without smiles
> without regrets
> but with civility
> 'Good night, Willie Lee, I'll see you
> in the morning.'

In search of Margaret Fell

And it was then I knew that the healing
of all our wounds
is forgiveness
that permits a promise
of our return
at the end.

* * * * *

[I] was Inquiring after the way of the Lord,
and went often to hear the best ministers that
came into our Parts, whom we frequently
entertained at our House many of those
which were accounted the most serious and
Godly men, some of which were then called
Lecturing Ministers, and had often Prayers
and Religious Exercises in our Family. This I
hoped I did well in, but often I fear'd I was
short of the right way.

The Puritan sought a personal relationship with God which would permeate every part of life. Faith demanded discipline and a constant examination of conscience. Salvation might be preordained but believers could not know if they were among the elect. All they could do was to continue to wrestle with doubt and conscience in the hope of God's grace showing itself in an unmistakable way. Illness, grief or suffering led to both heart-ache and soul searching. Across three centuries it's difficult to empathise. Ralph Josselin mourned the death of his infant son convinced that God 'hath taken away a son' because 'I have walked with much vanitie in my thoughts' and 'have given my mind to unseasonable playing at chesse'. How could Ralph have been to blame? God, for whatever reason, was three hundred years away from the invention of penicillin.

Thomas and Margaret Fell both sought truth in the words of the visiting ministers they invited into their home. Domestic piety was not enough of itself, nor was churchgoing. They needed ideas and interpretations of Scripture to guide their quest.

A travelling preacher arrives at Swarthmoor. Margaret regards her guest gravely. The man's face is chiselled, skull-like. It is difficult to meet his stare. When he pauses for breath or thought he flicks impatiently at strands of hair that fall across his face. The rise and fall of his voice is hypnotic: Margaret lets words flow over her. The preacher is a Genevan, Calvin's man; his view of salvation leaves no room for compromise. There are God's elect, the band of saints who will rule in heaven, but equally surely there are those God has damned. The visitor turns to his text.

> Examine yourselves, whether ye be in the
> faith; prove your own selves. Know ye not
> your own selves, how that Jesus Christ is in
> you, except ye be reprobates?

Margaret longs for the certainty that she walks with Jesus as she orders her household and arranges her days. Pious woman that she is, she knows how the passage continues.

> Be perfect, be of good comfort, be of one
> mind, live in peace; and the God of love and
> peace shall be with you.

It is what she aspires to, and falls desperately short of, in her marriage, in her family, in friendship and in the dozens of other relationships that are part of her life. As the preacher prays she asks God's mercy and comfort for those she loves and for those she has loved. Are election and damnation such certainties that they deny God's people the right to hope?

* * * * *

[Thomas Fell] was a Justice of the Quorum in his Country, a Member of Parliament in several Parliaments; Vice-Chancellor of the County Palatine of Lancaster, Chancellor of the Duchy Court at Westminster, and one of the judges that went the circuit of West-Chester and North Wales. He was much esteemed in his Country, and valu'd and honour'd in his Day by all sorts of People, for his Justice, Wisdom, Moderation and Mercy; being a Terror to Evil-doers and an Encourager of such as did well...

1641: Thomas Fell became a Justice of the Peace. The title pleased him; it gave him stature in the community. JPs tried criminal cases at petty and quarter sessions; they also regulated corn prices, fixed wages and directed such poor relief as there was. Thomas had his entry into the administrative circles of the County of Lancaster and a foothold on the ladder of political advancement. He was an ambitious man; moreover he had a family to provide for.

Thomas and Margaret Fell were entering the tenth year of their marriage. They had four, soon it would be five, children. Were they lovers or friends? Companionate marriage was much prized by the Puritan gentry as a harmonious background for spiritual and family life. It was a harmony maintained by women who regarded wifely obedience as part of their Christian duty. Thomas looked at Margaret and what did he see? He glimpsed the woman who could competently manage his affairs in his absence. He saw the pious, godly matron who cared for her children and servants. He saw wifely obedience. Perhaps he saw his lover. Did he see what moved her to laughter or tears, roused her passions or enlisted her sympathy?

Marriage and child-rearing were woman's appointed roles. Margaret raised Thomas's children. He allowed himself a moment of pride in his eldest daughter's quickness of speech and quickness at her letters. The little girls, Bridget and Isobel, overwhelmed him with their tumbling energy whenever they were released from the nursery world. In truth he often failed to tell one from the other, but then he was human rather than perfect. The intensity of the love he felt for his infant son had taken Thomas by surprise and still startled him. It was part of what fired his ambition. Land and the status that went with it would be his son's inheritance.

Thomas Fell, patriarch, sat in his hall at Swarthmoor and took stock of what was his. The hall, with its spacious comfort, would shelter future generations. His land was well managed; it provided much of the food on his table, wool and linen for household use, and surpluses that could be sold. His cattle, sheep and corn made modestly useful profits. But Thomas wanted more than this. It's easy to picture ambition as greed and criticise the pursuit of gain. Thomas Fell was no saint. He sometimes laid himself open to charges of wrongdoing. His much younger sister Alice accused him of defrauding her of her inheritance. The charges weren't made until Thomas was wealthy enough for his success to sting but their being made at all suggests a streak of ruthlessness in his make-up that can't have been easy to live with.

Yet ambition was only one side of Thomas Fell's character. The other was the 'godly magistrate'. Service and acceptance of the responsibilities that went with it were an important part of Puritan life. Thomas Fell and men like him knew that national crisis was approaching. They actively looked for a part in events, and a way of shaping changes that were by now foreseeable. Oliver Cromwell was never God's only Englishman. There were many more for whom, to be an official of any kind, was to be an instrument of God. It was these 'godly magistrates' who were the real revolutionaries of the 1640s, and who, in 1649, purged Parliament and ordered the execution of the king. They were driven by something more potent than ambition. In 1640 they found it possible to believe that God had deserted a nation that had lost touch with divine purpose. The need to rediscover that purpose was part of what drove them forward.

They were goaded too, by what they saw as the breakdown of central government. By 1640 Parliament had not met for eleven years. The Crown's opponents were beginning to talk of tyranny. What they feared more were the consequences of Stuart incompetence.

Charles I never understood the extent to which he was alienating his subjects. The High Church policies of William Laud, appointed Archbishop of Canterbury in 1633, had never been popular. Now Charles allowed the Archbishop to launch an outright attack on Puritanism in the mistaken belief that once an example was made Puritan preaching in the capital would end. William Prynne, Henry Burton and John Bastwick were respectable citizens, a lawyer, preacher and doctor. They were brought to trial in the King's court of Star Chamber in 1637 for protesting against bishops and the hierarchical structure of the Church of England. The sentence was harsh, even given the times. The three men were fined, whipped, mutilated and then imprisoned. The stern God of Puritan England could do nothing but align with Charles' political opponents.

In the same year, 1637, John Hampden's Ship Money case came to trial. Hampden was a wealthy man. Some said he was the richest commoner in England. Yet he refused to pay the paltry twenty-shilling tax assessment on his Stoke Mandeville estate. Charles needed money but not Parliament. His solution was the Ship Money assessments. They'd been successful too, with about ninety percent of the assessed sums reaching the Treasurer of the Navy. It was their legality that was questionable. Nobody queried the King's right to demand contributions towards equipping the navy from the coastal counties but Charles was levying Ship Money over the whole country. His excuse was the presence of pirates in English waters. Hampden's protest rested on a nice point of law. It also raised far-reaching questions about the extent of the royal prerogative. When the judges found for the King they seemed to be affirming despotism.

Thomas Fell and his Puritan neighbours didn't like what was happening in the south but they were powerless to stop it. They had the slight advantage of being far enough removed from the capital to have the protection of distance when they wanted to speak their minds in the safety of their own houses. They saw the fate of Prynne, Burton and Bastwick as martyrdom; they sympathised with Hampden and tried to fathom the full implications of the judgement. The Scottish crisis really alarmed them. Border raids were part of the folklore of the north. Northerners were only too aware of the likely outcome of upsetting the Scots. Charles Stuart was not. He thought he could impose an Anglican prayer book on a Presbyterian nation and in doing so he fanned flames that turned smouldering resentment into war.

Charles hurtled England into war against the Scots without the means to support an army. In 1639 he tried to collect both Ship Money and the army's equivalent, Coat and Conduct Money. The gentlemen of England, sensing the imminence of crisis, refused to pay almost to a man. The English troops that assembled at Berwick in June were poorly paid, worse organised and almost completely demoralised. It was not a force that would win an easy victory and renew Stuart popularity. Charles was brought to the point where he had to call Parliament. The Short Parliament met in April 1640. It was dissolved within three weeks by a King who was surprised at the intractability of its refusal to grant taxation without redress of grievances. Meanwhile the Scottish army reached Newcastle and Charles was forced to agree an armistice at a cost of £850 a day, a peace as costly as the war it ended. In November Parliament met again. The king's opponents had the advantage that goes with the power of the purse but there was no easy parliamentary victory. The jockeying for position, the bids to change the balance of power, the Remonstrances, Declarations, Propositions and negotiations continued for almost two years.

The Scots war was seen as the final proof of Charles I's ineptitude. The Puritan conscience, Parliament's belief in the 'liberties' of England, a kind of consensus among the opposition groups that the world was changing in ways the Stuart monarchy failed to acknowledge: all these combined to drive the country towards civil war.

A young woman sits in a college library, resisting the temptation to stare at the river meandering past the window and weave dreams. A biography of William Laud, Archbishop of Canterbury, is propped open on the desk.

> There are certain periods of history in which, on a superficial view, the actions of men appear to have followed rules entirely different from those with which the modern world is familiar…
>
> [Yet] the more we analyse the 'Wars of Religion', the less of religion, properly so-called, do we find in them. Indeed, it would be as easy to believe that the nations of Europe fought for four years over the death of an inconvenient Archduke, as that they ever fought for a hundred over the attributes of an unproven God.
>
> What then was all the fighting about? If religion be merely a doctrine about the origins of the world and the destiny of the soul, certainly it was not about religion, as neither one nor the other of these things could be altered by revolution. But if religion be the ideal expression of a particular social and political organisation as well (and observation shows us that men prefer to idealise their political ambitions for the purposes of defending them) then we can understand why men were once prepared to fight for 'religion' in a way they will not fight for it now, when most religions have shed their political implications.

It opened up the study of religion as a force that both defined and defied community and nationhood. Here I stand. I can do no other. The words are Luther's defiance of the might of the Holy Roman Empire and the church of Rome. Yet they sent Thomas More to the stake as well as Thomas Cranmer. They explain the lives of Oliver Cromwell, George Fox and Margaret Fell. If giving voice to these words constituted acceptance of a call from God then that acceptance was never given in a vacuum. It was given against the background of events, attitudes, ideas, wealth and poverty that is history and within the context of the complexity of suffering and joy that is all our lives.

Thomas was the lens through which Margaret viewed national events. He had more contact than she with those who held office in Lancaster and London and more opportunity to keep in touch with changing times and changing opinions. Thomas Fell's attitude to the monarchy was hardening: he seemed to be making allies of their more radical Puritan neighbours. His wife still distrusted the intensity with which these men criticised court and king, bishops and church and claimed to know the will of God. She did not join in their conjectures and feared the consequences of pressing their arguments to a logical conclusion.

Thomas Wentworth, Earl of Strafford, Lord Deputy of Ireland, was executed on Tower Hill in May 1641. Thomas Fell and his friends seemed to take a jubilant satisfaction in the event. Across the Swarthmoor dinner table the radical voices of John Sawrey and Thomas Birch welcomed the news. They dubbed Strafford 'Black Tom Tyrant', the most evil of Charles' 'evil counsellors'. He had been impeached on charges that claimed he 'did traitorously and wickedly counsel his Majesty to this effect: he was loosed and absolved from all rules of government…and that he had an army in Ireland which he might employ to reduce this kingdom.' Black Tom had plundered Ireland and threatened to use his Irish army to sack England. He was dead now, the first of Charles Stuart's robber barons to meet his end on the scaffold. The king would be the more malleable for his loss. God-fearing Puritan gentlemen convinced themselves that Tom Wentworth's death was a blow for freedom.

Margaret shared neither their mood nor their certainty. She could not comprehend this vengeful hounding of an opponent who had less chance of escape than a pursued animal in open country. Little good was spoken of Thomas Wentworth, but wasn't he just a man who served his sovereign as best he could, who had a family, who loved and was loved? His death had the appearance of a ritual act of vengeance. The trial dragged on for seven inconclusive weeks before

Parliament sent its victim to the scaffold by Act of Attainder. The Act was little more than judicial murder, no matter how the lawyers glossed it. If Parliament could stop a trial and condemn a man to death by its own will, what could it not do? Margaret shivered. This was the power to control people and events that she sometimes thought Thomas craved. Its possibilities frightened her. She retreated from the harsh expediency of politics into her own concerns.

Sarah, her fourth daughter and fifth child, was born in 1642. It was the first year of civil war. On 21st August, Charles Stuart raised his standard at Nottingham. The war bred bitterness. Neighbours and kinsfolk found themselves on opposite sides. Some Englishmen managed a kind of die-hard neutrality. It helped if you were poor and wanted neither the King's shilling nor Parliament's. Civil war, like government, was the preserve of the rich or at least the well born.

Religious creeds served to exacerbate political differences. Two-thirds of the Lancashire gentlemen who fought for the king were Roman Catholic. Three-quarters of those who fought for Parliament were Puritan. The parliamentarians were stronger in the north. For the most part they stayed to fight the war in their own county while their royalist neighbours rode south to the King's side. Thomas Fell had his brief moment of military glory. He was among the Puritan gentry who defeated the larger Royalist force in the skirmish of Swarthmoor. The battle was fought out on the open moor, away from Ulverston and Swarthmoor Hall. It was the nearest the war came to touching Margaret. She found her mind could not accept these new realities. She could not picture men she had known for most of her life meeting in open country, their swords drawn in anger. How did principles bring people to such a pass? She sensed the ruthlessness on both sides and felt no connection with it. Thomas argued that the king was a tyrant whose actions must be moderated by Parliament but Parliament at war looked equally tyrannical.

God had created turmoil in England. Men and women looked for explanations. Discovering God's purpose was a Christian duty. Enlightenment came in Scripture and sermon. A godly preacher sits with Thomas Fell locked tightly into a world of ideas. This minister is a sparse thin man, balding, black gowned and soft-spoken. Much of his talk is aridly intellectual. He has learning and Scripture.

Margaret takes her place on the window seat. She must do her duty by this guest of Thomas's and by her own soul. She struggles to learn from the preachers in the hope of finding order in this disordered world. This minister gives them no comfort. He offers them Job. 'Shall we receive good at the hand of God, and shall we not receive evil?' Now he begins his dissertation anew: mankind has broken its covenant with God. God's rod and God's wrath will strike at mortal hearts that know no contrition. Those who provoke God must humble themselves before him and seek the cause of His displeasure. It is only of His grace that God will renew that covenant and the roads back to grace are the hard roads of pain, punishment and true repentance.

Margaret searched her own heart and prayed that the word of God might reign there.

* * * * *

> I was one that sought after the best Things,
> being desirous to serve God, so as I might be
> accepted of him.

The war years frightened Margaret. She didn't feel physical fear. She had no doubts about Thomas's ability to protect her and the children. Indeed Furness and North Lonsdale quickly came under Parliament's control and there was little serious fighting in the area. Her malaise was of a different kind. There had been a time long ago, before she married Thomas, when she had felt the constraining influence of her father's house and her parish church. She had yearned for a wider world and more distant horizons. Now the boundaries had disappeared and with them her security. Lost in a country for which she had no map: she only recognised her own need for ritual through its absence. There had been no churching after Sarah's birth and Margaret felt strangely incomplete. The child had been baptised, she was loved, but something was missing from her welcome and from her mother's life. It was not just the comfort of tradition or even the affirmation of her motherhood: the rites of baptism and churching, the feasts of the church year, the taking of Holy Communion were all part of the way she expressed her sense of belonging to a community. In a country divided by politics and armies she was no longer sure where she belonged and the uncertainty alarmed her.

10th January 1645: William Laud, former Archbishop of Canterbury, died on Tower Hill. In March 1644 he was finally brought to trial after lying forgotten in the tower for three years, a sick old man who had robbed the English church of its purity. A merciful Parliament allowed him to die by the executioner's axe. Laud's death was symbolic rather than necessary. Revolution pursued its course relentlessly; no quarter was given.

14th June 1645: The battle of Naseby. The decisive conflict of the Civil War was fought on the outskirts of an English village, a set piece battle: Cavalier against Roundhead. Prince Rupert's Royalist troops stood little chance against Cromwell's New Model Army. It was all over by nightfall. Victory went to the prayerful, sermon attentive soldiery of the New Model. There were relatively few deaths; the Roundheads took 5000 prisoners.

Returning from New Zealand in the mid-seventies, I came home to the alien land that was village England. We lived in Clipston. Prince Rupert spent the night before Naseby in the thatched house next to the primary school, or so the story goes. Mellow Northamptonshire stone glowed orange in the sunlight. Fields were hedge bound; autumn meant blackberries. There were meadow flowers in May and June. Cattle were pastured at the end of the lane; tractors rumbled past the door. History was to be had for the asking. In the parish church of the hamlet of Hazelbeach the register began with the record of infant deaths in 1801. The country houses of the still royalist gentry were open to the curious on Sunday afternoons in spring and summer, Spencers' Althorp, Brudenells' Deene, Ishams' Lamport. My sons raced through grassland yellow with daffodils under the branches of ancient oaks. I remained a visitor, waiting for the holiday to end and reality to start. At Rushton, in the early seventeenth century, Thomas Tresham built the Triangular Lodge, three, by three, by three, affirmation of a Catholic Trinity and statement of a steadfast Roman faith in a Protestant England. What shape is indifference or uncertainty? Say 'I am too busy just now' or 'I don't know' in bricks and mortar if you can.

August 1645: The Long Parliament had been in session since 1640. Its membership was dwindling. The exclusion of Royalists made the house ridiculously small. Parliament called the recruiter elections of 1645 to make up its own numbers with men of the right persuasion. Thomas Fell became MP for Lancaster; the godly magistrate was called to serve on the national stage. As a member of the County Committee for Sequestration, investigating the value of Royalist land holdings, he had already achieved some local prominence. Ambition and service met as Thomas rode south towards the Palace of Whitehall confident that he could influence events.

Margaret was left at Swarthmoor. An estate without a master needed its mistress. She managed the land, her household and her children. In the twilight of early evening she sat with her account book entering neat columns of figures. A plough shaft had been repaired, the barn roof patched. Small surpluses of butter and cheese were sold in Ulverston market. Michaelmas would bring the need to pay wages. Routine provided stability. It allowed her to concentrate on what was manageable and near at hand. Swarthmoor was an orderly world. Keeping it so shielded her from the chaos elsewhere.

There is comfort to be had from domesticity; from clean linen and tidy space, from the order we bring to our daily living. Miracles happen in kitchens. Knead dough, set it to prove and the bread will rise. Make jam from gooseberries and the colour will change from the green of the berries to a deep burnt orange. It's one way of creating the illusion of control.

Margaret found safety in life's continuity. The household religion that had been a central part of her own childhood was now part of her children's lives. She wanted them to have its support in a world where change and novelty came too rapidly. They needed the framework of Scripture to know their own truths about right and wrong, privilege and responsibility. And despite the way her own beliefs were being shaken by the uncertainty of the times their mother had a core of faith to pass on to them and to share with the rest of her household.

> The grass withereth, the flower fadeth; but
> the word of our God shall stand for ever.

And if the word of God was to stand forever its resting-place would be in the hearts of all God's people. Margaret looked for a God of love, not a God of battles. It was love that she wanted to shape her relationships with her husband, her children, her friends, neighbours and servants, the infinite love of the Christ of the Beatitudes.

> Blessed are the merciful: for they shall obtain
> mercy.
> Blessed are the pure in heart: for they shall
> see God.

Margaret Fell struggled to find the purity of heart that would see God in the dawn and the sunset, in the first growth of spring and in the fullness of harvest, in her children's smiles and their laughter. Often she succeeded but she was never sure it was enough. The simplicity of the message seemed out of step with the times in a divided country, where the God of Parliament and Puritan raged against the God of the King and the established church. The enemies of the king were God-driven but Margaret did not want to face the might of a God who led armies, nor could she comprehend a God who brought out the ruthlessness in men. She trembled before an all powerful, all frightening deity and acknowledged her own frailty. She saw again the painful desolation in her sister's eyes the last time they met. She let the image go, but through it she saw her own weakness. And in that weakness she saw her need of God.

Yet, almost perversely, Margaret had ceased to think of herself as physically vulnerable. Five healthy pregnancies and five healthy children had made her confident. She saw no reason for the pattern to be broken and her preparations for the next birth were matter of fact. She was used to the rough kindliness with which the Swarthmoor women helped her through her labour and she wanted no other. This birth was no different. Her body knew what to do. Her second son was born easily. Margaret registered the infant's first cry followed by a woman's voice repeating the words of the old sacrament of baptism, words condemned as superstition in this newly Puritan England. It was dreamlike but it was real. Through the pain of the after birth Margaret understood that the mucus-covered infant had been baptised with his father's name. She could not understand what had prompted the action. Her son's cry had been healthy enough. Margaret held him close searching anxiously for warning signs. Not finding them, she allowed herself to hope and to pray.

The babe had a contented nature. He had plenty of distraction too. His sisters chattered childlike to the small bundle in the wooden cradle, drawing the first smiles and gurgles from the new arrival. The child was happy and he was loved but he did not thrive. His mother could not pinpoint what was wrong and tried hard not to admit that there was anything. Tomorrow or next week he would suddenly grow and she would take him out of swaddling clothes. But tomorrow came and next week passed and there was no change. Margaret dare not let herself think he was slipping away out of her reach, but she had no cure for the sickness that afflicted the infant as the year dragged down towards the solstice.

At first he cried, an awful hurt cry that denied comfort and ended in the sleep of exhaustion. As he became weaker he quietened. He lay

In search of Margaret Fell

on her breast but he could not feed. He vomited, not baby posit but some acrid smelling substance. She tried to suckle the whimpering bundle; she did not know what else to do. She clung to the tiny body as if she could force life back into its fragile frame. There was no healthy tug on her nipple and she watched another trickle of vomit run down the tiny chin. She felt the fevered skin through the swaddling clothes. The heat bound mother and child together. The babe barely whimpered now. She knew he could not live the night but she did not want the knowledge. Tiredness, born of childbirth and anxiety, gripped her. Her own body ached. She adjusted her weight in the low nursing chair, unable to relax and release the pain of waiting. Briefly she thought of Thomas, in London on England's business. Was this small death her business alone?

She could do nothing except watch now. Numbed, she waited. She watched and listened for the slightest movement that betokened life. There were so few. The small fist weakly clenched and unclenched. She was almost sure an eyelid fluttered but she did not know. She held her cheek close to the infant face, willing herself to feel his breath. She dozed and woke and dozed again and fought the exhaustion of the early hours. To know the moment of his passing was the only token of her love she could give this child. Afterwards she thought she heard the clock strike as the infant's breathing ceased but she was never sure. In her blackest moments she was certain that she had failed the child. It seemed that he had died because she had not had the energy to will him back to life. God had questioned her invulnerability. Numbness was her defence, the only way she had of easing the pain.

Three hundred years later another woman sat curled uncomfortably on a cottage sofa nursing a sick child, afraid that the crisis would come at the moment when her body refused to fight off sleep. But the twentieth-century morning brought a doctor and an ambulance and a siren blaring dash through a winter dawn. She waited again, that other woman. Now there was a surgeon and his houseman and a team of nurses: there was knowledge and technology. There was no need for God. She waited through another night and she did not have to search for signs of life. A machine monitored and echoed the tiny heartbeat; lights flickered on a screen. She could not hold the child. There were drips and tubes and a small face made old by a mask of sticking plaster. Somewhere, in a tinsel decorated corridor, a choir sang Silent Night. On Christmas morning a young nurse, her uniform decorated with the gaudy glitter of the season, left a small Christmas stocking topped with a red woollen bobble. I didn't want to celebrate Christmas. Thirteen years later all that remains is a minute white scar on a firm, young belly and a dusty, ragged woollen bobble, symbol of despair. And, just occasionally, the memory of numbed emotions surfaces painfully.

Thomas returned in time for the burial. They stood together in Ulverston church: man and wife, master and mistress. The world saw the couple. It did not see the fence between, but the fence was there, built of different experience and the separateness that it produced. Something more than miles divided London from Swarthmoor and kept Thomas Fell MP apart from his wife.

'In the midst of life we are in death', Margaret tried to pray. She could not find the meaning behind the words. She did not comprehend the justice of a God who could take such a frail, new life. 'Examine yourselves whether ye be in the faith,' enjoined the scriptures and the Puritan preachers. She did not know why she had been sent such pain. Had she not loved enough or trusted enough?

She examined her own life. She punished herself by conjuring imaginary wrongs she might have done tradesmen or tenants or servants. She asked herself again and again if she had always been fair in her treatment of the children. She loved them; was she sometimes too hard on them? Did she expect too much of her eldest daughter simply because she was the eldest? Battles over unpicked stitches and blotted script seemed scarcely worth the winning. She thought of her sister, still childless, still maintaining a precarious hold on reality, or so she imagined. She could not know because she did not visit. She did not want to confront this shadow side of herself but she knew it for part of her failure, her sense of sin. Nor did she want to examine her relationship with Thomas at this moment. His absences and his ambition disturbed her. She was his wife yet he constantly pulled away from her. It was as if her belief that she had failed the dead child had infected all her relationships. Love had failed her.

Midwinter 1645/6: The Furness hills were bleak. No snow fell, just a bitter cold sleet. The countryside was painted in shades of grey. It was a world without colour and almost without daylight. Candles, tapers, rush lights and the sparks of wood fires provided a faint glow and a faint warmth. The people ate salt meat and bread made from the dwindling stocks of summer corn. Skins grew pallid and tempers frayed among those confined too long and too closely within doors. Parliament had decreed that Puritan England should not celebrate Christmas. There was no crack through which hope could enter this world of darkness.

Thomas returned to London. Margaret managed Swarthmoor with a kind of automatic competence. There was little to do except wait for the spring but diligently she gave orders for linen to be darned and store cupboards rearranged. She cared for the sick on the estate when winter brought its burden of illness and accident. Her children were growing up. On one grey afternoon she marked their heights in a row at one corner of the nursery wall. She tried to concentrate on loving them. Proudly or shyly according to their natures they recited lessons learnt or played music newly mastered. It was in such quiet pleasures and the accomplishment of everyday tasks that healing lay.

The milestones of my sons' growing up. A nursery rhyme read from a book held upside down. Riding a bike without stabilisers for the first time. Cricket bats and footballs. The teddy bear put carefully away in a cupboard. There was a fall from a bike and gravel embedded deep into a forearm, a bank holiday spent in casualty. The crash and slam of them leaving the house on dark winter mornings to do their paper rounds. First trips abroad, first term at university, degree days. The battered Metro parked proudly at my gate. The phone calls: 'I've reached Seattle and I've got a cold.' 'I'm in Manchester and I've been mugged.' ' I might come and see you.'

In 1646 Thomas Fell was named a Presbyterian elder for the Furness district, recognition of his local standing rather than a reflection on the state of his soul. Presbyterianism was meant to be the new establishment but it was only ever established in London and Lancashire, where Parliament was strong. Elsewhere the parish churches were Baptist, Independent or Presbyterian as chance and local preference ordained.

Margaret Fell, mistress of Swarthmoor, wife to Thomas Fell, MP and Presbyterian elder, knew her duty. She sat in a church stripped bare of ornament and image by force of law and gave sermons and expositions of scripture the hours of straight-backed attention they demanded, but her soul was untouched. There was no gentleness and little love in the message she heard from the pulpit. The fatalism almost suited her mood while she carried the bleakness of the child's death. She struggled with what she saw as unyielding language and doctrine. Election and reprobation, salvation and damnation were hard words, however they were explained. Margaret was cowered by the frightening face of God that they presented and longed for compassion. She would struggle with her own conscience and her own sense of sin but she could not imagine a God who would refuse her grace. Surely her infant son had not been condemned from the moment of his birth by an all-powerful but unfeeling deity? Churchgoing fed her despair. She had lost the authority of the old church; she could not accept that of the new.

Helplessness was the lesson of one short life. Margaret Fell was still the Lady of Swarthmoor who had the means to give coppers to the poor, and the rank and position that went with wealth. The gentlewoman could not put herself in the place of the labourer's wife but she began to see her world more clearly. As she rode back from Conishead and the stiff formalities of a social call, men working the fields respectfully raised their hats to her. A woman adjusting the bulk of her pregnancy in a cottage doorway, a child on her hip, contrived a deferential bob. A beggar sat at the crossroads; even the woman on horseback couldn't avoid seeing the sores on his legs. A tinker family was encamped on the common; three scrawny children playing in the dust, a woman rummaging hopelessly amongst a sparse cart-load of possessions. Before nightfall the constable, fearful of plague or a charge on the parish, would move them on.

Anna Marie was a Traveller's child, two years old, almost three. She stood staring at me with dark Romany eyes. There were gold rings in her ears and silver bangles on her wrist, a gold chain about her throat. She wore rumpled white socks and an oddly formal pink frock with a white sailor collar, more old world than Laura Ashley. One grubby finger was raised to pick at the eczema sores on her face. She continued to stare. I was teaching her mother to read. That was two summers ago. Now the site where they parked their trailer is derelict, destroyed by vandals and bullies and a borough council only too ready to give up mediation and rebuilding, and let Travellers move on.

Statute and ordinance tried to keep vagrancy within bounds, not put an end to suffering. The only assurance that pain and despair would not last forever was the word of God. In the prophetic imagery of Revelation the bleak darkness of destruction was pierced by the blinding glory of the light of God. At the end of time the Kingdom of God would come into being in a shape and form that denied imagination. Did the might of God first have to destroy this England?

> ...lo, there was a great earthquake; and the sun became black as sackcloth of hair, and the moon became as blood; and the stars of heaven fell unto the earth, as a fig tree casteth her untimely figs, when she is shaken of a mighty wind.

In the language of metaphor, God warned his people and sent them signs and portents: the woman in labour, clothed in the sun; the red dragon with seven heads; the serpent and the beasts; the lamb and the angels; the whore clad in purple and scarlet, and the fall of Babylon. And God's people believed that their world would make way for Christ's kingdom.

There were many who preached the Second Coming. The scholarly Ralph Josselin studied the Book of Revelation with the help of Thomas Brightman's *A Revelation of the Apocalyps*. First published in 1611, Brightman's was the most widely read of contemporary commentaries and one which offered plenty of scope for millenarian speculation. Predicting a date for the Second Coming demanded mathematical as well as theological leaps. Ralph recorded his calculations.

> ...at night my heart settled much expecting within a short space of 3, 4 or 5 years to see Christs worke against the beast much advanced, and that on these grounds. From 395 when the Beast and Kings arose to 1656 are just 1260 dayes or apocalipticke yeares: to 1653 are 6 times Adam's age who dyed at 930: which is annus mundi 1580 – 1656 in the same yeare after Christ in which the world was drowned after the creation that being anno mundi 1656.

Now it seems like a fantasy game played with a random set of mystical numbers. Then it seemed perfectly possible that a God who could destroy the social order of centuries could also institute his own at a preordained time. It was a theology born out of despair. Ralph Josselin began his study in the dark days at the end of the year. It was 1650. Money and food were scarce. In May the Josselin's daughter Mary had died. She was 'eight years and forty five days old'. In June they buried the second of their sons to die in infancy and Mary Church, their closest friend in the village of Earls Colne. To those who suffered, Revelation offered hope of a different kind of future. Ralph Josselin clung to it.

> Behold, the Tabernacle of God is with men, and he will dwell with them, and they shall be his people, and God himself shall be with

them and be their God. And God shall wipe
away all tears from their eyes; and there shall
be no more death, neither sorrow, nor
crying, neither shall there be any more pain:
for the former things are passed away.

I crossed Aldgate High Street by subway. The stairs stank of urine and stale
beer. The underground corridors were dimly lit. No footsteps echoed but
my own. Turning to regain daylight I became aware of a figure squatting
against the far wall. For seconds I was alone and threatened, but threatened
by what? By this other's stillness, his silence, by the hat pulled down onto a
face that avoided all contact? Or was I refusing to confront the gulf between
my wealth and his poverty? Weighed down by handbag, purse and credit
cards, I climbed the steps to the street. The figure sat on in a private realm
bordered by three black plastic rubbish sacks and a Sainsburys carrier bag.
Was he waiting for release by act of Parliament or by act of God?

In London, Parliament grappled with the problems of government
raised by the need to deal with both the King they had defeated and
their own rebellious, unpaid army. Thomas Fell moved cautiously.
Membership of the Commons was small. Even after the Recruiter
elections of 1645 average attendance was only about 150. Thomas
had no hope of remaining quietly anonymous while he sounded
opinions and formed his own. His support would have been actively
sought. In the event he had little choice about where he gave his
loyalties. Thomas Fell was not prepared to put his trust in Charles
Stuart. He thought it naive to assume that the King would sign away
his power in the ways outlined by the Newcastle Propositions and
other halfway proposals; and further to presume that if he signed he
would keep to the agreement. That being the case Thomas was
compelled to place his trust in Oliver Cromwell, already the warlord.
But even for Cromwell there was no obvious course of action. Civil
war had produced no tidy solutions. Frustration mounted; suspicion
and fear were rife. The idealism of 1642 was lost. The hope of

shaping a new Jerusalem that had sent Thomas Fell elated on his way south in 1645 evaporated quickly. He did not want to sully his hands or his reputation with the political realities of the time. Like others of his colleagues he left London for home in 1647. Perhaps he already feared that he would have the King's blood on his conscience if he stayed. Perhaps his ambition was thwarted by the muddle of post-war government.

These were wilderness years. England was ruled by 'Saints' but deserted by God. In 1646 and the four succeeding years the harvests failed. Crops did not ripen in wet summers. The north of England was less badly hit than the south but the effects of famine were felt everywhere. The numbers of poor and destitute grew. There were more requests for alms at the Swarthmoor door; more craftsmen whose lives foundered on other men's misfortunes; more premature deaths. There were men and women who took to the roads, begging a day's labour here and coppers there. There were those who travelled with misfortune and those who travelled with ideas. Radicalism was a wayside gospel. Levellers demanded political equality and Diggers equal rights to the land. Ranters and Seekers promised equality before God. And as George Fox 'was walking in a field on a First-day morning, the Lord opened it to me that being bred at Oxford or Cambridge was not enough to fit and qualify men to be ministers of Christ'.

* * * * *

September 1647: Thomas Fell arrived at Swarthmoor at dusk, tired and angry because of the way he had punished himself by crossing the Sands on the late tide rather than break his journey in Lancaster. Margaret had word of his coming. There a chain by which Furness knew who was riding across the Bay. She had time to prepare herself for his arrival but she was less eager for this homecoming than others. The speed of his departure after the infant's burial had bruised her more than he could know but she had learned to

In search of Margaret Fell

deal with her own grief. Accustomed to her solitude and to her authority within her household she was loathe to relinquish either. She remained standing by the great fireplace as Thomas made a noisy, almost blustering entrance. He was not entirely at ease either. She heard the greetings he called to servants. From the staircase came the excited squeals of the children. Margaret caught the words 'father' and 'London' and 'presents' and became impatient with the drama of it all. The door was thrown open and he was before her, still clutching hat and gloves. Of course she was pleased to see him; after fifteen years of marriage she still needed his physical presence. She was glad of his return but she held a part of herself back. Her muscles tensed and as the children tumbled into the room she moulded her face into an indulgent smile.

When they are alone Thomas's talk of London is as sparing as his letters have been. Margaret contents herself with asking after acquaintances but she senses the aggression he is trying to contain. She finds his mood difficult to read and more difficult to respond to. She tries telling him Swarthmoor news but he seems uninterested. Abandoning him to his own thoughts she picks up a piece of embroidery and sits frowning at its delicate pattern. He impatiently arranges papers and sets himself to absorb their contents. At length they retire, he still moving with the heavy hurried strides of exhaustion, she trying for a calm she does not feel.

Margaret senses the danger in the air around her husband in those first days after his return. She knows he is making decisions; she wishes she had his confidence. Confronted with the power he cannot use elsewhere she is forced into retreat.

Thomas Fell remained in the north but he looked south almost obsessively. What he saw happening gave his conscience no respite. In October 1647 the rebellious, and unpaid, New Model Army assembled at Putney. The army council had been infiltrated by the radical egalitarianism of the Levellers, men with whom Thomas Fell, man of property, had no sympathy. The new year found him with even less sympathy with the revival of support for the king that led to the brief renewal of hostilities known as the second civil war. Cromwell rode north and defeated the royalist die-hards at Preston. Charles Stuart remained a prisoner on the Isle of Wight. Parliament could not long put off deciding his fate.

30th January 1649: In Whitehall Charles I, King of England, died on the scaffold. This execution was the climax of England's revolutionary drama. With a stroke of the axe King became martyr: his kingdom a Commonwealth. Was the nation nearer the Kingdom of God for that? Regicide: the killing of the King. Many of Charles's subjects were shocked at this so logical conclusion to the battle against absolute monarchy. But they were no longer subjects. Nor were they citizens, a concept that wasn't to be invented until 1789. Power in Commonwealth England rested with Cromwell and the army grandees. In the counties it was still the landowners who ruled. The change in leadership did not affect the chain of command. Masters and landlords were still masters and landlords. Labourers still sold their labour. Beggars were still dependent on the charity of the rich. The faithful might look to the priest or minister. But now that a King no longer sat on the English throne by the grace of God, all other certainties were less than certain. Political, religious and social assumptions were called into question. For the moment the questions could be asked. There was no censorship.

There had been no negotiating with a monarch who clung to the royal prerogative, no way of achieving a fair or even workable division of power between crown and Parliament. Thomas Fell and others like him, their hands untainted by royal blood, were relieved that the decision had been made.

30th January 1649: The dark cold of winter lingered but the days were lengthening. Aconite and snowdrops bloomed. The woman at Swarthmoor prayed for Charles Stuart's soul.

In search of Margaret Fell

> ... the healing
> of all our wounds
> is forgiveness
> that permits a promise
> of our return
> at the end.

She allowed herself to picture a world without enmity.

In a world in which an established church had less and less place Thomas Fell explored ideas that allowed the individual to determine the nature of his own faith. The religious boundaries were down. The paths were no longer clearly marked and the signposts conflicted. The university-trained clergy no longer had a monopoly of prayer and preaching. Men, and some women, of all conditions and occupations published their own truths.

A travelling preacher finds his way to Swarthmoor's door, a mechanic who can mend a plough shaft as well as preach a sermon. This visitor has found his faith among the Baptist congregations of the midlands. He has no time for the Presbyterian church order, asserting the right of lay Christians to form churches and choose their own ministers. When he finds his stopping place he will call his own gathered church into being. His is not the narrow doctrine of predestination. Christ Jesus is the light of his world and of his heart and 'as many as received him, to them gave he power to become the sons of God, even to them that believe on his name'. It is a simple truth he has to share. Margaret almost understands the source of his faith but she retreats from possibilities inadequately voiced. He speaks it enthusiastically and directly but when he calls upon his hosts to join him in extempore prayer they are united by their silence. Forms and notions still prevail at Swarthmoor; they offer safety.

Thomas Fell was the Commonwealth's man. Idealism gave way to pragmatism. The Rump of the Long Parliament continued to act as the government but it was the army command who ruled. The King's death did not stop the killing. Oliver Cromwell set out to silence the opponents of the new regime. He had no choice. More martyrs were created. Army Levellers mutinied and four low ranking officers were shot, as an example, in Burford churchyard. They died heroes. History has preserved the bullet marks on the church walls. The bloody massacres of Drogheda and Wexford taught the Catholic Irish that English rule was merciless. A year later the Scots were given a similar lesson at Dunbar. Being Protestant, they were treated less harshly. There was less killing; instead, the English took prisoners they couldn't afford to feed. Twelve months later the uncrowned King Charles II was defeated at Worcester, God's 'crowning mercy' to the Commonwealth. Cromwell's England had security of a kind.

Once, long ago, I went to Greenham with Penny, Odette and Liz. It was golden October. The trees hadn't shed their leaves. It was a walk in the sunshine, the screech of military tyres, humour that carried a barb, tea made on a camping stove, cut wire and solidarity. Somewhere lurked the warheads that could destroy our enemies or our world. How much of it was make-believe? Long years afterwards I went back with other women. Grey February cold. A slashed and tattered fence. Empty space. Deserted silos. Fairy rings on the grass. A solitary military policeman intent on showing us the right way out.

The warlords could not rule without the support of the county communities. Thomas Fell and the Puritan landowners of rural England were an important link in the chain of national order. They served as MPs and civil servants, administering the counties. They became JPs, sat on County Committees and aspired to be sheriffs or lords lieutenant. Thomas Fell became Vice Chancellor of the Duchy of Lancaster in 1649. The same year he was nominated attorney for the county and shortly afterwards he was appointed an assize judge. No salaries went with any of these offices but there were fees and perquisites and inside information and the opportunity for financial gain.

Thomas Fell bought land. It was always a sound investment and there was a kind of gratification in adding acre by acre to the Swarthmoor estate until it reached the boundary with Marsh Grange. In the end

In search of Margaret Fell

his empire straddled the peninsula from Morecambe Bay to Duddon Sands. People talked. What war profiteer doesn't encounter suspicion? The rise in the Fell fortunes was too fast not to attract attention and Thomas was making money from the misfortunes of men who had rallied to the King's standard in 1642.

Thomas Fell was one of a small group of Lancashire gentlemen who profited from post-war land sales. His activities and those of his business associate Thomas Birch were noticed. Birch appeared rather too often at Swarthmoor for Margaret's comfort. She liked him no more now than she had at their first meeting nearly twenty years ago. There was a single-mindedness about the radicalism that drove him and an edge to his ambition which she found threatening. His intimacy with Thomas might be worrying but her husband was no child to be rescued from ill-chosen friends. Margaret's welcome lacked warmth but it was given.

Parliament, in need of money, not least to pay its army, sold land that had once belonged to crown, church or Cavaliers. Thomas Fell and Thomas Birch made their purchases. Something over a thousand pounds changed hands. It was a lot of money to find in 1650. There were whispers suggesting the deal might not have been above board. Then Thomas Fell made his coup: nearly five thousand pounds' worth of land bought with forged debentures, or bills of credit, came into his possession. Birch contented himself with a more modest killing. The gossip was rife then. Margaret was isolated by it. Her neighbours talked less easily to her now and she could not fend off accusations that were never quite made.

Mistress Fell profited by her husband's increased wealth. She bought silk and fine merino wool for her gowns. She could indulge her elder daughters' taste for ribbons and laces. Swarthmoor's hangings were changed and she took pride in the thick tapestry that would protect her from the fierce winter winds. There was a new oak chest in her hall and new carriage horses in her stable. Gossip was always short-lived: this storm would die down. Margaret held her head high but she continued to worry. She wanted peace with her neighbours. Her eldest daughter was almost marriageable. Moreover, she worried about Thomas and what he was doing to himself. She saw the godly magistrate being destroyed by the man of affairs.

They had been married eighteen years. It was half Margaret's lifetime. She wanted Thomas's companionship, not the ferocity with which he attacked work and acquisition and prayer with equal relentlessness. She conceived another child and knew not whether the act of conception had been one of love or anger. Later Margaret saw their mating as part of a struggle Thomas was waging with himself.

The war years had benefited Thomas Fell. He was never blind to that. His star would not have risen so high under Stuart rule. Swarthmoor, with its income of £150, was a fairly modest inheritance. Kings ever had the support of men of higher birth and standing than Thomas and rewarded them in return. Thomas Fell had the ambition and the energy to chase after power. Equally, service to the state was part of his calling and, for all he did and was, he answered to a Puritan conscience. It was an uncomfortable combination. 'Examine yourselves, whether ye be in the faith.'

Thomas Fell wrestled with himself. He lived in a world where rewards for services were not set by contract. Office entitled him to fees and perquisites that formed a large part of his income. Besides which he was industrious and more honest than most in his working life. He tried to live up to his own ideal of the 'godly magistrate' serving the nation as the instrument of God but he wanted evidence of success. He needed the people who pointed to Judge Fell, man of wealth and property, as well as those who praised him for the nice balance of his legal judgement. With Margaret he was ever courteous and affectionate but guarded. She was his wife, not the keeper of his conscience. He would settle his accounts and ultimately work out his own path to salvation but he would do so on his own terms.

Thomas still needed ideas as he needed meat and bread on his table. Preaching excited him but so did work. He rode out on the assize circuit, was in Lancaster or London, was home but riding the bounds of his estate, and was gone again. His wife lived in the wake of his energy and found no peace. They seemed to fence with one another. Domestic life was a series of formal moves. The Fells were trapped inside a drama that was not entirely of their own making. The play would reach its climax, but how? And when? Margaret played her part, acting out days: wife, mother, lady of the manor. She felt her nerves grow taut. The will to respond quietly to husband, children, servants was something she achieved with enormous effort. She seemed to step outside herself and watch another woman going about her life. Her watching self saw love and care given to a household, hospitality given to guests, comfort given to the sick or grieving, charity given to the poor. The watcher saw a woman alone, not a woman led by God. Watching, Margaret became aware of the longings of her own soul. She sat in church or lecture, attentive and hopeful; she left disappointed. With her household she prayed but no answers came. Alone, she tried to form the prayer that expressed her yearning but no words came.

Providence determined the lives of men and women and of nations. England had dethroned the Stuarts and was ruled by the sword. Did the fall of a monarchy herald the last days? Thomas Fell appeared to have forsaken God for avarice. Had God forsaken him? His wife, sensing herself deserted by God, sank into her own dark night's journey.

> This know also, that in the last days perilous times shall come.
>
> Therefore is the anger of the Lorde kindled against his people, and he hath stretched forth his hand against them, and hath smitten them and the hills did tremble, and their carcases were torn in the midst of the streets.
>
> How long wilt thou forget me, O Lord? For ever? How long wilt thou hide thy face from me?

There was no comfort in the Bible, just the bleakness of despair. Margaret walked her own wilderness without trust, without God.

Her spirit took refuge in nightmare. The imagery of biblical prophesy filled her dream world. The dragon and the beast appeared pawing the air and bellowing wildly. She thought she saw the figure of a man, no features just the outline, and a white hat against the darkness. The dream was always dark, the suffocating brown-black of the forest, until the moment when the light burst forth, blinding her, terrifying her. How she willed the daytime world to return! Let the silhouettes of furniture resume their third dimension; let life resume its ordinariness!

The play in which Thomas and Margaret Fell were trapped did not reach its climax. They became better actors almost convinced of the truth of their own script. Thomas buried his guilt and Margaret battled to ignore her restlessness. Swarthmoor arrived at its own kind of domestic peace. Tensions gave way. Life settled into a pattern of normality. In 1651 the gentle Will Caton arrived at the Hall to be a companion to George Fell. Young Margaret was a woman of eighteen and the baby Susannah beginning to pull herself upright on the furniture. Bridget, Isobel, Sarah and Mary laughed and cried, quarrelled and were reconciled and grew up. Margaret thanked God for her blessings and willed anxiety and dreams alike to recede.

1651 brought England a dry summer and a better harvest. There were still itinerants and vagrants, made rootless by the times or their own will. The Rump of the old Parliament still ruled; Oliver Cromwell continued to wield the power of the sword. It was an uneasy truce between government and governed. The fire had gone from the revolution's elite. It burned among the people. There were still Levellers daring to press for an egalitarian end to revolution. Ranters saw God on street corners. Fifth Monarchists preached prophetically of the power and terror of living in the endtimes, and of the second coming of Christ which would be now. George Fox was released from Derby jail 'and then the light and truth and glory of the Lord flowed and spread abroad'.

There was no national church. William Lampit had the living of St Mary's with Thomas Fell's approval. Lampit was a Cromwellian, an

Independent in politics and religion, who had a reputation as a fiery preacher. On Sundays and Fast Days he could expound scripture for three hours or more together. William Lampit's views were firmly held and forcefully expressed. He had no fear of confrontation. Thomas Fell wanted to share Lampit's scholarship but was not prepared to see his pulpit as the fount of all wisdom. The judge continued to explore the edges of faith, taking his wife with him on journeys into uncharted territory. Margaret, her sensitivities heightened by her awareness of the space in her soul, sought vainly for a message or an idea she could respond to.

A traveller reaches the shelter of Swarthmoor as the evening light begins to fade. He is made welcome and dines. This man wears the hodden grey of the north-country farmers. As he addresses his hosts he slips into the 'thee' and 'thou' of their own district. He is not a university man, he tells them. He does not claim learning. His features are roughened by exposure to wind and weather but his face is open and honest seeming. A Seeker is how he describes himself, one who seeks his own way to God. Like the Fells, he has seen the church change from old ways to new. Now he has no patience with any forms or notions and will have none of the church or its sacraments. Instead he meets together with friends to read the Scriptures and discourse of religion; often they wait silently for some sign of God's will. His way demands no Presbyterian discipline but an open heart, a love of God and a willingness to do God's will. God's mercy is assured; the believer must listen to the promptings of the Holy Spirit at work in the heart to know that mercy for her or himself. It was for the individual to live their life in the face of God and under God's guidance. The traveller gives them Deuteronomy for a text:

> The eternal God is thy refuge, and under-
> neath are the everlasting arms.

And he gives them the prayer that is in his heart.

Thomas likes the visitor for his candour and simplicity but the idea of faith without discipline is as alien to him as that of life without work. His God shows wrath and dispenses justice. The judge clings to Presbyterian discipline: he wants to know the holiness of God but he does not want that knowledge as a gift. He would earn it. His is not the God of the Seeker meeting. And his wife? The preacher's simple goodness touches her heart. His assurance of hope comforts her. But the Seeker's very benevolence stops her belief. She cannot give credence to a message preached in humility without passion. She will know her own truth by the power and fire of its expression. Revelation will bring the painful illumination of her dreams not quiet comfort.

What was I seeking then? Not church nor faith but an escape from life's edges and a sense of belonging. I thought it was simply a matter of putting down roots. This is the tenth house of my married life; it was going to be the last. I was going to belong here. Was I looking for community? But community is a very elusive concept, not easily taken hold of and stored away.

Diggers and dreamers: the first work party on the Spring Lane Reserve. Clearing derelict allotment land to create shared open space. Corrugated iron sheds, tin baths, ancient rusty mowers, an enormously heavy roller, defunct buckets and watering cans. A half-won battle against the brambles. For forty-eight hours it was a neighbourhood project, about people and places, rather than ecology and local politics.

Godmanchester Meeting House. It must be ten years ago. Community as a dream in which perfectionism eventually smothered practicality. The beginning was special. For a while the group kept in touch. I still have the last newsletter and a dusting of optimism and hopefulness, the conviction of a better way.

* * * * *

> I declared the everlasting truth of the Lord,
> and the word of life... showing that the Lord
> was come to teach his people himself, and to
> bring them off from all the world's ways and
> teachers, to Christ the true teacher, and the
> true way to God.

Fox came over the hills in mid-summer, his own vision of God's truth clear in his mind and firm in his heart. He came into Furness, walking easily, in step with his purpose, looking down at the farms and fields and people. The days were long and the sun was high.

The year had been dry; hay-making would be over early. The grass was beginning to parch. Margaret's countrywoman's heart was lightened by the season. Corn stood high in the fields and cattle grazed the meadows. Harvest would replenish store-cupboards: this winter would see less hunger.

Fox strode down into Ulverston through the bustle of the town, stared at and staring, passing the church and the ale-house, leaving market place and cottages behind 'and so to Swarthmoor and Judge Fell's'.

Mistress Fell was out and her 'Husband was not at Home, being gone to London'. Fox stormed into the presence of their children and William Lampit, curate of Ulverston, who 'would talk of high notions and perfection and thereby deceived the people. He would have owned me but I could not own him nor join with him, he was so full of filth.'

Margaret rode homeward. Movement matched the restlessness of her spirit. She made herself concentrate on the things that bound her to Swarthmoor. She was returning to her children, to the hope of a letter from Thomas, to music practices and supper, prayers and Bible stories. Domestic tasks and small pleasures would continue to be her lot: she knew no other way. Yet, turning in at the Hall gates, she had a fleeting sense of giving the people who were her life here into someone else's care. She allowed the feeling to become a prayer and commended Swarthmoor and all who lived within its bounds to God's keeping.

What greeted her was a babble of voices, as her children vied with one another to relate the scattered fragments of a story that wanted nothing of drama or excitement. There had been a confrontation between William Lampit, whose preaching had struck fear in more hearts than theirs, and a stranger. The two men had bellowed at one another in this very room. The stranger was huge, bear-like, untameable. He belonged on the hills, not here within doors. He denounced a world of darkness, the lie that was the church, the devil's advocate in priestly garb. He assumed the authority of the prophet, the harbinger of Truth. The children were compelled to listen, awe-struck but uncomprehending. Their mother found herself suddenly insecure. Was this God's moment of revelation to her? She dared not think so. She was the lady of the manor: William Lampit was her minister. She must not allow him to fall victim to the attacks of an itinerant who had no place in this community. Her children needed the assurance of calm and certainty. She fought down the spectre of emptiness, of faith that was mere habit. She longed for God to invade her heart and soul and possess her as he must surely possess this stranger. Yet she was so sure of her own weakness that she did not want to be tried and found wanting.

> So at night we had much of reasoning and I declared the Truth to her and her family.

> ...it pleased the Lord in his Infinite Mercy and Goodness to send George Fox into our Country, who declar'd unto us the Eternal Truth, as it is in Jesus...

Truth, Light, Power, God: Margaret willed this to be an illusion. She feared it was a reality beyond time or place and she trembled before Fox's conviction. The anxieties and uncertainties she had been trying to hide from herself returned. When prophet once more attacked priest, she heard truth strike at falsehood and thought she saw steeples topple and church walls crumble. Dream images of a light that blinded and darkness that terrified resurfaced to disturb her. She did not want to walk this nightmare land. Hers was the grey world of the everyday, where convention ruled. She sought refuge in small tasks. Her hands filled with the silks and books, toys and trinkets that were the clutter of family life and impatiently scattered them again. What did domestic order matter?

On the next Fast Day, Thursday 1st July, Margaret and her children went to service at St Mary's.

Thursday, 1st July 1652: market day in Ulverston. In the square they traded on for coppers and small silver regardless of the summons to church. Cottagers' wives, who counted survival in farthings and half pence, willed butter not to turn in the heat. A beggar urinated in the gutter. Livestock bellowed, the noise belying their skeletal frames. A drunkard raised a flagon of ale to his great slobbering mouth and called obscenities after a serving maid. The reply came in kind, the crude banter of the streets, but the laughter of the bystanders had an uneasy edge to it. The day was sultry. Tempers would fray. Bargaining would become bickering; fists would be raised.

> Soon after a day was to be observed for a humiliation, and Margaret Fell asked me to go with her to the steeplehouse at Ulverstone, … I replied, 'I must do as I am ordered by the Lord'. So I left her, and walked into the field; and then the word of the Lord came to me, saying, 'Go to the steeplehouse after them.' When I came Lampitt was singing with his people; but his spirit was so foul… that after they had done singing I was moved of the Lord to speak to him and the people…
>
> And the first words that he spoke were as followeth: 'He is not a Jew that is one outward, neither is that circumcision which is outward, but he is a Jew that is one inward, and that is circumcision which is of the heart.' And so he went on and said, 'How that Christ was the

Light of the world and lighteth every man that cometh into the world; and that by this Light they might be gathered to God', etc. And I stood up in my pew and I wondered at his doctrine, for I never heard such before. And then he went on, and opened the Scriptures, and said, 'The Scriptures were the prophet's words and Christ's and the apostles' words, and what as they spoke they enjoyed and possessed and had it from the Lord'. And said, 'Then what had any to do with the Scriptures, but as they came to the Spirit that gave them forth. You will say, Christ saith this, and the apostles say this; but what canst thou say? Art thou a child of Light and hast walked in the Light, and what thou speakest is it inwardly from God?'

This opened me so it cut me to the heart; and then I saw clearly we were all wrong. So I sat me down in my pew again, and cried bitterly. And I cried in my spirit to the Lord, 'We are all thieves, we are all thieves, we have taken the Scriptures in words and know nothing of them in ourselves'…I saw it was the truth, and I could not deny it…

A woman stood alone before God, led by God to this moment of confrontation. A woman stripped of privacy and dignity who found Truth in the raw exposure of her inner self. A woman who wanted nothing so much as to be left alone with the mystery that was God and the churning of her own emotions. A woman for whom the sting of tears on her cheeks was an unwelcome reminder of the concerned stares of her children and the curious looks of her neighbours. A woman, fired by a vision of God at work in the world, who wanted to hide in the cloak of her own domesticity. She could not flee: neither carriage nor Hall could give her shelter.

In St Mary's the drama unfolded as it had to. John Sawrey won his point and Fox was evicted from the church. Undeterred he preached on in the churchyard 'and after came up to Swarthmoor Hall'.

God sent me no moment of revelation. Instead, She nudged and prodded and beckoned me forward. I travelled in a foreign land, unable to read the signposts. I found inspiration in people I met on the way, in words and pictures, sights and sounds. I picked up clues and took years to piece them together. I inched my way forward, alone yet not alone.

* * * * *

At Jacob's Well a stranger sought
His drooping frame to cheer
Samara's daughter little thought
That Jacob's God was near

This ancient well, no glass so true
Britannia's image shows
Now Jesus travels to Britain through
But who the stranger knows

Yet Britain must the stranger know
Or soon her loss deplore
Behold the living waters flow
Come drink and thirst no more.

The woman then left her water pot, and went
her way into the city, and saith to the men,
Come, see a man, which told me all things
that ever I did: is not this the Christ?

Jacob's Well: the Samaritan woman faced God and, in God, she faced
herself. In laying down her burden she discovered her purpose. In
her return to the city lay her way forward. There was no choice and
she was afraid. Through her fear she learned trust. Tentatively she
walked the path of the Jew, Jesus of Nazareth.

* * * * * *

For the love of God Margaret Fell cried aloud in Ulverston church.
In the days that followed she cried silently. Convincement brought
her scant comfort. Fox's insistence on the worthlessness of images
and symbols, of formal prayer and the mechanical reading of
Scripture forced her back into herself. Margaret would walk in the
Light of God but her first steps were the faltering ones of an infant
striking out after a bauble dangled just out of reach. She was caught
fast in God's shadow as she wrestled with Fox's words.

> You will say, Christ saith this, and the apostles
> say this; but what canst thou say? Art thou a
> child of Light and hast walked in the Light,
> and what thou speakest is it inwardly from
> God?

Struck dumb by God's power and her own fears, Margaret could say nothing. She knew God had chosen the path that this so unworthy servant should follow. She could not admit that knowledge. She was still Judge Fell's wife, her children's mother, Swarthmoor's mistress: Margaret held her whole life in tension and implored God not to make her choose.

Mistress Fell waited for her husband to come home. She was not so blind to the world around her that she did not realise that the town talked. Fox, driven by God's urgency, soon travelled beyond Swarthmoor, but his companions, Richard Farnsworth and James Nayler, remained as guests in her house. Margaret was unsurprised when John Sawrey and his friends rode out across the Sands to greet the returning Judge with the news that his household had been bewitched. She knew Thomas had little time for gossip and she did not really think he would condemn her unheard. But so great was her own inner turmoil that she lost sight of his rationality and she did not know what she expected. Fragments of imagined conversation assailed her. When Thomas reached home it was his lack of words that troubled her. There was so much that needed to be said. Her husband appeared oblivious to the need, wanting only to eat, drink and recover from his journey. He knew Fox's associates were in the house and Fox himself was expected but he had no desire to converse with the strangers at his hearth. Thomas's polite calm became more than Margaret's nerves could bear. She was no actor for all that she had rehearsed the words and set the scene. She sat with Thomas as his meal was served making meaningless inquiries about his well being to which he gave only the briefest of answers. A man exhausted by work and travelling and the effort of parrying his neighbours' suspicions, faced a woman for whom the tensions of waiting had become too much. They avoided the contact that would propel them into discussion and from there into conflict. Margaret's attempts at conversation stumbled to a halt. The strained silence was broken only by the sound of the children at their music in the next room. For once there were no parental words of pride or encouragement. Wrong notes jarred on taut nerves. When the music practice stumbled to a halt the silence echoed.

Margaret had neither shouted, nor wept. She sat still and seemingly in control, wanting a sign, though of what she did not know. She had never been so conscious of herself, nor of a power beyond herself. She knew God in herself and what it was to be possessed by God. She knew both belonging and surrender. She lost herself in the mystery that is eternal and recognised it for the reality of her life now and for always. Afterwards she was never sure what had taken place: what remained was her awareness of God in the moment, and God in her. 'And whilst I was sitting, the power of the Lord seized upon me'. Thomas was 'quiet and still'.

Even without his robes of office Thomas Fell was the judge. His right to determine events was never questioned. George Fox returned and was received by the master of the house. The man of property stood face to face with the itinerant. The godly magistrate faced the man of God. The eternal seeker was confronted by the man of conviction. Margaret could do nothing but listen to the scene being played out before her. Outwardly courtesy and good sense prevailed. Thomas used his temporal authority as protection against enthusiasm and excess. The judge was in control, keeping the conversation within the bounds of the world he knew and understood.

> Art thou that George Fox that Justice Luke Robinson spoke so much in commendation of amongst many of the Parliament men?

It was a simple question. It afforded Fox the respect that was his due, but it demonstrated Thomas Fell's worldly connections. Fox was seemingly undeterred, intent on proclaiming his truth; now he couched it in language the politician might use. He 'opened Christ's and the apostles' practices, which they were in, in their day. And he opened the night of apostasy since the apostles' days, and laid open the priests and their practices in the apostasy.' Thomas found his spirit rising in response to the passion in the other's voice. A less complicated man might have given way but Thomas Fell could not give heart and soul to ideas his legal mind would not endorse. He recognised Fox's prophetic power but his own image of God remained so tightly bounded by covenant, law and discipline that he could not accept this vision of truth beyond all reason. The seeker was not convinced. A troubled man was left facing Fox. There was not, and would never be, a dramatic conversion. In the last resort Thomas Fell could no more declare himself another man's follower than Fox could bend his knee to any secular power. When Margaret wrote about the encounter she was an old woman. She had forgotten the tensions. She remembered Thomas as 'the kind friend to Friends', not as the judge of whose verdict she had once been as fearful as any prisoner at the bar.

> At Night G. Fox spoke so powerfully, and
> convincingly that the witness of God in his
> conscience answer'd that he spake Truth; and
> he was then so far convinc'd in his Mind that
> it was Truth, that he willingly let us have a
> Meeting in his House the next first Day after,
> which was the first Publicke Meeting that was
> at Swarthmore, but he and his men went to
> the Steeplehouse.

The judge was a public figure: Thomas Fell was a private man. Nobody need know how painfully his decision was arrived at.

Standing in the gulf that separated two men and striving to find a relationship with both, Margaret wrote extravagantly to Fox, 'thou bread of life, without which bread our souls will starve. O, for evermore give us this bread, and take pity on us, whom thou hast nursed up with the breasts of consolation.' The words she used with Thomas were those of the long married. Pragmatism had more place in their dialogue than extravagance. They were still a couple with shared responsibilities, with arrangements that had to be made and obligations met. Margaret sensed the judge was treating her with clemency. His manner towards her had a formality that took her back to the first months of their marriage. Then it had made her feel like a child: now it made her feel a stranger. She ached for him to understand, to experience God's presence as she did, to share her conviction. As they sat opposite one another at table Margaret was forced to confront the concern in Thomas's eyes. She lowered her own. To reject his love tore at her being: to own it was to be its captive. Through the deep dark of winter nights compassion drove her into Thomas's arms but her loving carried the sharp edge of impatience with the bonds that tied them. Afterwards she lay stiffly at her husband's side, the clay form of a woman whose heart and soul were elsewhere.

By the spring Mistress Fell knew she was pregnant. The familiar symptoms, the nausea, the soreness, the dull ache in her lower back, brought relief of a kind. Margaret almost welcomed this chance to return to a life she understood. Her husband's stern features rose before her. Thomas lowered his guard and she came face to face with the ageing man beneath the judge's robes. She forced herself to acknowledge the fatigue, the lines of strain and worry, the concern. Thomas and Margaret Fell, man and wife. God would not – could not – drive them apart. The children, the house, the land and its people were the product of two lives. Margaret dreamt her memories and knew they were Thomas's too. She willed herself to push them aside and, with them, the carefully weighed arguments and moderate tones of her husband's voice. It was not reason that would guide the next part of her journey but conviction. The voice of the living God came to her as fragments of instruction that she struggled to interpret. Fear gripped her: her muscles tensed and she became conscious of the taut skin across the mound of her womb. The unborn child turned and kicked.

Rachel, her seventh daughter and eighth living child, was born in October 1653.

> ...And if I have faith in all its fullness, to
> move mountains, but without love, then I am
> nothing at all.

Without love, I am nothing. Love is the suspension of self. Love is the need to give. Love sears, love hurts. Love is the violent urgency of sexual desire. Love is both passion and compassion. Love is trust. Love is the fear with which the soul confronts the presence of God. Love is the ability to walk away and to walk alone.

We can walk side by side, together but apart, and you cannot follow me. You cannot share the depths of my despair nor the heights of my heart's yearning. You have no window to my soul. You cannot enter my dreams. Do not try. That is love and those are the spaces in between.

* * * * *

There were two men whose loneliness Margaret could not ease. The second was her only son. He stands awkwardly before her, an over-grown child still despite his fifteen years. Margaret looks at the length of wrist protruding below stained cuffs. She takes in the scuff-marked boots, and the defiance in his eyes and resorts to fussing over the open trunk on the floor. Thomas would make a lawyer of the boy and has enrolled him at his own Grays Inn. London is so far away and George such an unpromising student! Alas, confidence and diligence are not in her gift. She tries to counsel him to give good attention to his studies, to keep out of bad company and away from those who would drink or gamble. She does it badly; finding no words for this half-grown, wary man who looks set to shrug off her caresses. At last she can only bid him tidy himself for the journey, and mourn the alacrity with which he flees from her presence.

Alone, she needlessly refolds a shirt, smoothing imaginary creases out of white linen. Would that its owner were as easy to handle! She sighs, remembering George, hurt, bruised and tearful, in flight from the Ulverston mob who would damn him for a Quaker. She would have her son convinced, but she wants his safety and his happiness. Might London be kinder to him! And let God send this son of hers success that Thomas might be proud of him.

* * * * *

First Day meeting in Swarthmoor's great hall. Margaret Fell struggles to still her mind, to banish errant thoughts. God's light and power are here: she would have them invade her being. Around her the quiet bustle of arrival continues. She becomes aware of the youthful figures of her daughters, the serenity of young Margaret's smile and the frown that creases Bridget's brow. The room fills. A woman, perspiring still from the walk across the fields, the hem of her skirt streaked with mud, glows with exercise and expectation. A farmer, head bowed and shoulders sagging, mind a-buzz with figures from the account books left spread on his kitchen table, longs to lay down his worldly cares. The daughter and sister of an estate labourer sick of fever sit close together, heavy-eyed with worry and lack of sleep. An Ulverston carpenter, his wife and child, keep close to the door, unsure of their welcome. Later arrivals force them forward: they melt into the meeting. The Swarthmoor servants squeeze a path through the crowd. The youngest among them looks ill at ease, bewildered. Why is she here? There is a single, sharp intake of breath. Then silence. The meeting becomes as one. God is among them and in them.

Words are spoken. Prayers offered. The gulp of a woman determined not to weep breaks into the silence: her tears fall. An old man, white-haired, rocks himself and sways from side to side. The all-revealing light of God bears down on His people. They know both agony and ecstasy. A woman rises, speaks in broken sentences, a volley of words that means nothing but conveys much. The lace that adorns her bodice rises and falls as her heartbeat quickens. She tries to wipe beads of sweat from her face but cannot raise her hand. Her legs feel incapable of supporting her weight, yet she remains standing. She is overcome by shivering, by trembling, by quaking: the Holy Spirit enters her and speaks through her.

I want to break through the barrier of time and hear her words. I want to stand beside Margaret Fell and experience the presence of God as she did. All I can do is use her images to frame my prayer.

God is the 'Fountain of Light', the rainbow unwoven. God is the red of blood. The scarlet of poppies. The blue of the Virgin's robe in a medieval Book of Hours. The bold red, blue, green of a child's painting; the glare of the city's neon. The hurt brown of my lover's eyes. The grey mist-hung dawn of the fens, black loam of fields, yellow beam of headlights at a railway crossing.

'And if you love the Light, then you come to the Light to be proved, and tried, whether your Works be wrought in God.' The light is God, all powerful, all revealing. The single bulb in the prison cell: the prisoner cannot flee. 'Let the Eternal Light search you... it will rip you up and lay you open... naked and bare before the Lord God.' I must peel away the masks: status, occupation, race, creed, to know myself – to accept myself, to change myself? Standing before God both powerless and empowered but held fast, unable to move, awed into silence and stillness. 'And on the invisible wait in silence, and patience, and in obedience to that which opens the Mystery of God...'

The mystery of God, present here, in this moment, as I put these words on to this page. Present in the moment of creation, of birth, of artistic truth.

The inexplicable mystery of God revealed in the life of Jesus, the prophet and teacher. 'God hath sent forth the Spirit of his Son into your hearts, crying, Abba Father.' Christ has come to guide his pilgrim people. 'Where Christ hath given you Light, walk in him, learn of him, who is lowly, who is meek; and be swift to hear, slow to speak, and slow to wrath....' Jesus the story teller. 'For the woman that hath lost the Groat, sought without; but she found it not, till she came to sweep her own House, and there she found it.' The 'unswept and unclean' house of the soul. In the debris lies the grain of truth, 'the simplicity which is in Christ'.

I seek the purity of God within myself, the 'measure of Light', which is both God's being and God's gift. 'In your measures of the Living Light and Life of the Living God, wait low, and in the fear of God stand faithful to your own measures.' I seek my own truth, my own path. I would understand humility. I would take hold of faith in order to live faithfully.

In the beginning was the Word, and the Word was with God, and the Word was God. It is 'this Word which we have seen, which we have heard, which our hands have handled'. To handle the Word in the living of my life is to bear witness to faith, to step out on a pilgrimage towards the unknowable.

Alone, I founder on my own shortcomings, my own inadequacies, the impossibility of ever pushing the boundaries of thought and action beyond myself and my self interest. 'So God Almighty be your Strength, Wisdom and Counsellor, and cloath you with the Armour of Light'. The power that is God, the empowerment that is God.

In the midst of a worshipping community I discover my strength. 'Dwell in Love and Unity, in the pure Eternal Light, there is your Fellowship.' Through the act of worship I reach out towards God.

* * * * *

> ... but he and his men went to the Steeplehouse.

Thomas Fell sits alone in his family pew. His neighbours stare at the empty space beside him. Mistress Fell is no longer 'of this parish'. Women who expect her to be there when they wait for a birth or a death find that she is not. Hopeful mothers of sons who expect her to bring her daughters on matchmaking calls find that she does not. Margaret Fell still lives at Swarthmoor Hall but she is in a far country. The 'great people' George Fox has gathered are her people now.

To them she writes,

> And Friends, your Day of Calling is come; ye are called out of the World, and separated from the World, by the Call of the Living God.
>
> ...Now consider, how you hearken to this Holy Call, and how you are obedient to it,

In search of Margaret Fell

and how you are subject, and how you are
taught and guided, by the measure of God's
Spirit...

For he that walks in the Light, as he is in the
Light, the Blood of Jesus cleanseth from all sin.

Her old self was no more: she had been made new. She too could be
made perfect in God as long as she allowed his light to push and
goad her, to force her to disown sin and the falsity of the world.

Oh! Once she had danced the dance of manners expected of people
of her rank. She remembered a grand gathering long ago. Was it an
earl or a lord who had honoured Furness with his presence? She saw
herself sinking into a graceful curtsey before him, her smile fixed. She
had called him 'Sir' or 'milord' and used the formal 'you'. Why had it
taken her so long to see how empty such words were? The 'thee' and
'thou' of plain speech were all she needed now. More recent scenes
replayed themselves: servants greeting her as 'mistress', men doffing
their caps, shopkeepers paying homage to the gold coins in her purse.
She took the respect, if respect it was, for granted.

God called her to stand aside from the privileges of rank as surely as
he called her to condemn those of the church. She needed neither
this false church nor its grasping priests who claimed the tithe of
each man's income. There was no justice in a church that must be
supported thus. Yet it was the church Thomas continued to support
with his presence and she remained Thomas's wife. Her anger, her
need to be done with falsehood, burst not from her own lips but in
the scrawled words of a child's dream. Her daughter Mary wrote to
Priest Lampit in God-inspired fury,

The plaiges of god fall upon thee and crush
thee as dust under the Lord's feete how can
thou escape the damnation of hell.

It was truth from the mouth of a babe. The false church must be van-
quished to make way for the true. The days of apostasy were coming
to an end. Babylon would fall. There would be a New Jerusalem.

Oliver Cromwell, too, had a vision of the New Jerusalem that could be built in England's green and pleasant land. He experimented with 'godly' government. In the summer of 1653 the Barebones, or Nominated Parliament, was summoned to Westminster. Its members were godly men from the congregational churches and the shires. They threatened to abolish tithes and reform the law: Cromwell, distrusting their radicalism, sent them home. In December the 'Instrument of Government', Britain's only written constitution, made the Lord General Lord Protector. Protector Cromwell shared his authority with a Council of State, on which many thought the army over-represented, and a single chamber parliament. To some it was military rule, to others monarchy thinly disguised. Like later revolutions, this one had a conservative thrust.

The new constitution allowed liberty of conscience to 'such as profess faith in God by Jesus Christ': it excluded Anglicans and Catholics, whose beliefs were symbols of the old order. Yet Anglicanism survived where it remained non-political. The diarist John Evelyn made his Christmas and Easter communion throughout the Protectorate period. He was arrested briefly in 1657 but otherwise escaped notice. It was the radicals who attracted attention.

In Ulverston market they traded on. Butter, eggs and honey were sold for half-pence and farthings: cottagers' wives kept the wolf from the door. Trinket sellers made coppers from the world's love of finery. A peddler, the leer on his face directed at a courting couple, displayed ribbons and lace. At the churchyard gate the old crones muttered and gossiped. The townsfolk, for the most part, continued to attend Sunday service. William Lampit could still preach a fiery sermon and they were used to his ways. Ulverston had no time for the Quaker George Fox nor for the strangers who followed him across the Sands. What likelihood that God's word could be proclaimed by men and women burdened by few of the world's goods and none of its airs? It was as well to see Christ in the guise of beggar or vagrant. A crowd collected to stare readily enough. Sometimes the power of prophecy held an audience captive but it was a reluctant captivity. A suspicious crowd, listening unwillingly, feeling itself threatened, easily became a mob. And there were always those who would manipulate the mob.

> The people were quiet, and heard me gladly, until this Justice Sawrey (who was the first stirrer up of cruel persecution in the North) incensed them against me, and set them on to hale, beat, and bruise me. Suddenly the people were in a rage, and fell upon me in the steeple-house...

Fox was not the only victim. Mob and magistrate alike feared the Quaker menace.

> Mary Akehurst, a religious Woman of Lewis, going into a Steeple-house there, and asking a Question of the Independent Preacher, after his Sermon, was dragg'd out by the People, and afterward beaten and puncht by her husband, so that she could not lift her Arms to her Head without Pain...

> Richard Hubberthorn and others were taken out of a Meeting, bound Hand and Foot, and so carried and laid in the open Fields in a cold Winter Night.

> Rebecca Lucas, Widow, about eighty Years of Age, and her Daughters Rebecca and Mary, were summoned to appear before the Mayor of Hadleigh, who charged the old Woman to suffer no more Meetings at her House, nor to lodge any Quakers, threatening to quarter Soldiers on her, if she did....

Crossing London by tube, I change trains at Oxford Circus. A tall woman, black-skinned, sure of herself and her God, stands in the carriage doorway and preaches salvation. At Warren Street she declaims a prayer. God's chosen people rustle the *Evening Standard*, the rest of us look at our feet.

Dare I preach to a world that will not hear?

* * * * *

> And I was but young in the Truth, yet I had a perfect and a pure Testimony of God in my heart for God and his Truth. And I believe I could at that day have laid down my life for it.

The thin sunlight of late afternoon deepens into dusk. The wild geese fly over in a perfect 'V'. Margaret watches from her window, half-conscious of the pattern of wings and birds, half lost in thought. The conversation of her elder daughters reaches her, the eager tones of young womanhood. The infant Rachel shrieks in delight. Other voices mingle with theirs: Will Caton's tenor; the deeper, country-bred tones of John Camm; Gervase Benson, expansive, optimistic even; the high pitched concern of a woman she can't name. There would be news surely, letters collected from Lancaster. Her mind races with names and faces, well known and loved or but half-remembered. She thinks of all those who have set off from this house to publish Truth through the length and breadth of England. (Later they would be dubbed the Valiant Sixty.) Fox's emissaries and God's!

She is no preacher. It is not her calling to travel in God's name. Other women do so. Margaret remembers Elizabeth Hooton's weather-beaten face and defiant stance. She'd taken to the roads despite the opposition of the farmer husband who damned her for a misguided fool. More than once she'd fallen victim to the magistrate and suffered imprisonment. Margaret flinches. Thomas protects her still. His protection is God's gift, part of God's plan. She is sure of that. She must accept it for it allows her to do God's work. Swarthmoor is a safe harbour for Friends in a hostile world. News can be exchanged here, spirits and bodies nurtured. This house is at the centre of events so huge her mind can scarce encompass them.

Margaret pauses to smooth hair and skirts, an action that is the habit of years. Hurrying now, she rejoins the noisy bustle of her household. Newcomers are enfolded in the warmth of her welcome. She clasps hands, kisses cheeks, presses one to stay for a meal and another to stay overnight. She inquires after the health of families, the well-being of neighbours, the faithfulness of meetings.

At last she picks up the packet lying on the table, a fragile sheaf of words that could so easily have fallen into the hands of thief or government spy. This company is as avid for news as she. Young Margaret, Bridget, Will Caton draw closer. Conversations falter to a halt. Margaret cannot keep the emotion from her voice as she reads the letters aloud. Fox's Publishers of Truth, a battle-scarred band, send news of the war now being fought in England.

> There is many in this city hath desires begot-
> ten in them, but dare not show it, the perse-
> cution is so hot, and in the country round-
> about there is a shattered people which is
> coming in.

> ...all this city is on fire, but the power of the
> Lord chains all under;...here is such a noise
> among the dry bones, the time of their resur-
> rection is at hand.

Margaret knows their faithfulness and their resilience. She knows too their need to be assured that they are not alone. The Lamb's War rages in her head with every letter she receives and writes. Her words come from God: for so many they are an inspiration.

> You were elected before the foundation of the
> world was, and now are chosen and called
> forth to be faithful to the Lamb, who is now at
> war and shall have the victory, in whose battle
> you are now engaged to fight under his ban-

ner and to follow the Lamb wherever he goes. Oh my dear ones, who are the dearly beloved of my soul, unto you my life and strength reacheth, yea, ye are present with me, you in me, and I in you, never to be separated, earth nor sea, death nor hell cannot separate that which God hath joined together.

Even so ye are called in one Hope of your Calling, where there is one Lord, one Faith, one Baptism, one God and Father of all, who is above all, and through all, and in you all. And as the Lord hath loved you with his everlasting Love, and visited you, and hath made manifest his Eternal Light in you, which is the way that leads to the Father, and hath raised up the Eternal witness in you of his Everlasting Love. So let that Love constrain you to love one another; and that everyone may be made willing to suffer for the Body's sake, and that there may be no Rent in the Body but that the Members have the same care over one another.

Those letters survive, carefully mounted in leather bound volumes. A public record, written now in even lines of script; now with heavy strokes made by an impatient hand anxious to be done and moving on. The ink is brown and blotted: the paper a dull ivory. The books smell of age, with a hint of scholarship. Holes show where a seal has been hurriedly torn open. Words are scored out. The sense changed. Here the writer has filled the margins. Here only a fragment of the original remains. The text is difficult to follow, the language archaic, the biblical imagery obscure. Sometimes I catch the urgency, the compulsion to shout aloud and be heard. Sometimes, for a moment, I share the glory, sometimes the world-weariness.

Through a glass darkly I see a woman sitting at a desk, paper, pen and ink before her. Her head is bent low over her task. She does not look up.

In search of Margaret Fell

> ...my Deare unfained Love is to thee and tho
> I never saw thy face, yet thy Spirit I know and
> feel...

She warms Friends with the fire in her heart as surely as she bids them warm themselves at Swarthmoor's hearth. She understands their needs as certainly as she understands those of her own household. Love and inspiration are not enough. To do God's work in the world they must have food in their bellies, strong boots and warm clothing. Thomas does not often question the household accounts but sometimes she reads alarm or irritation in his manner. She refuses to worry. God will provide winter fodder enough no matter how many horses they shelter for visiting Friends. Yet Thomas should not provide all the money.

By the summer of 1654 Margaret had set up the Kendal Fund, a common purse from which Friends' needs could be met. Its creator received the accounts: 2s 6d for shoes, 2s 8d for britches, 3s 6d for a 'kase of knives'. Small sums and humble purchases, but without them many would not have survived. Margaret gave generously: she also exhorted others to give. It wasn't easy. For some Friends any request for money was dangerously close to the church's demand for its tithe. As more and more Quakers ran foul of the authorities so the need for help increased. The Fund could not be abandoned. It expressed unity with those who suffered need or imprisonment for Truth's sake. It demanded constant work.

The translation of faith into action. Is it so very different now? I try to recapture the energy with which I once sought to celebrate belonging with activity. I baked cakes for shared meals. I sold bric-a-brac and plants from market stalls, and later counted piles of copper and small silver. I sat on committees and organised public meetings. It spoke of empowerment, of belief in our ability to bring about change. It was a small, stumbling step on the road to the Kingdom.

* * * * *

> ...here you are found worshipping the imag-
> ination of your own Hearts, which the Lord
> God declares against ... therefore cease from
> your abominations, and turn to the living
> God, and him dread, and him fear, who is the
> dread of all Nations, at whose presence the
> mountains shall melt, and the Hills be
> removed, and the Rocks rent

Margaret grappled with ideas that would not be confined to paper. The year was 1656. She was writing to Manasseth-Ben-Israel, rabbi to the Jewish community in Amsterdam lately come to London, and through him to the Jewish nation. These strangers must be brought into the light. England was 'the land of gathering where the Lord God is fulfill-ing his promise'. Jew and Gentile would be reconciled and God could come again. Why else had Oliver Cromwell agreed to re-admit the Jews more than three hundred years after Edward I had expelled them?

1656, some called it the apocalyptic year. Men expected miracles or chaos.

> ...some thinke the very world would end in
> 56 others the beginning of good dayes to the
> church, but I expect troubles on the earth
> and thereby persons making themselves
> great, who in themselves or successors, will
> and shall deepely afflict the lord,

wrote Ralph Josselin, secure in his Essex parsonage.

Aren't there always troubles on earth and persons making them-selves great or others who would make them so? There are some who dare whisper of offering Cromwell the crown. Will the English have King Oliver if they are denied King Jesus? The Protector is content to rule not reign.

The parish clergy call days of National Humiliation and Public Fast. They would have their flocks cleansed. Village England complies after a fashion, and after that fashion prepares to meet God.

The apocalyptic reality is so simple the world refuses to see it. God has gathered a people who dare stand in his light, who dare confront their own fear and the reality of their own failure, who dare surrender their lives to God that they may be transformed. Christ has come again, not as the Son of God, not as the one pattern and example for all humanity; but as the Christ of the heart come to teach his people from within. In the daily lives of His people God speaks.

Bristol, 24th October 1656. No middle-eastern sun brightens this Palm Sunday. The dull grey of autumn's ending; rain dripping from the eaves of houses; the roads churned with mud. Pedestrians curse the carts of farmer or tradesman. Into the city comes a ragged procession, a pitiable mummers play. Christ-like, James Nayler sits astride his horse: his disciples cry 'hosanna' or 'glory' and strew the way with garments. A dog sniffs cautiously at a discarded shirt. A few passers-by stop to stare. The constables arrive to arrest the 'Son of Man'. Their laughter is mocking as they swear they will see the Quaker come again in Bedlam.

James Nayler continues to walk the way of the cross. This all too human Passion has not ended yet. He is tried by a parliament out to stop sectarian excess, and convince Protector Cromwell of the evils of liberty of conscience. The barbarity of those who sentence him knows no bounds. James Nayler is whipped through the streets of two cities, London and Bristol. His tongue is bored through and his forehead branded with the 'B' of blasphemy. He stands long hours in the pillory, the butt of the world's jibes. When his tormentors are done with him they despatch him to 'the hole' in Bridewell.

As Nayler is pilloried one Robert Rich nails up a makeshift, home-made sign, 'This is the King of the Jews'.

James Nayler was condemned by God to wrestle with a gift of prophecy that recognised no boundaries. Those who listen push faith to its limits and step into the abyss of the unknown and unknowable.

Margaret cannot understand, nor can she sympathise. She has not been in London, has not heard James preach, does not know how much of his fragile self he has given to God's work. There are women enough who hail him as saviour but she is not one of them. He is her 'dear Friend' still; he was one of her guides towards Truth; but his ministry strikes fear in her heart. He has surrendered to a call that is derided as madness, bringing the wrath of the law and the scorn of the world upon Friends.

Margaret tries to turn the Bristol tide with a letter appealing for James's loyalty. It never reaches him but it matters little. Mere words cannot halt a man driven to the edge by his God or his demons. Fox, imprisoned in Launceston jail, is as helpless as she. Margaret hardens her heart. It is left to James to write to her.

> My fear is of provoking the justice of God
> without mercy, through not showing mercy
> one to another.

She gives him no quarter. Her refuge is political pragmatism: this gathered people can have but one leader and it is not James Nayler.

* * * * *

> ...and fearfull lyes and storys they raised up
> against us: but ye Lord preserved us faithfull
> to him – And we kept our Integrity and mett
> together at our house att Swarthmore with
> my Husband's Consent: and he being Chief
> Magistrate in the Countey, they could not fall
> upon us in persecuting us as their hearts
> desired.

> We liv'd together twenty six years, in which
> time, we had nine Children. He was a tender
> loving Husband to me, and a tender Father to
> his Children, and one that sought after God in
> the best way that was made known to him.

Margaret shared Thomas's bed and his table. She scarce noticed that she was doing so. She was his wife: she tended him. She ordered the red wine of Bordeaux that pleased his palate: she had new wax candles placed in his study. She tried to remember when he was on circuit and when he was in Lancaster: she did not always succeed. When she thought of him, it was with the ache of sadness. He would not cross the line that now divided them and she could not retrace her steps. In God she loved him and counselled him.

> ...be faithful unto death and he will give thee
> the crown of life, and stand firm and close to
> the Lord and be not afraid of man. Greater is
> he that is in you than he that is in the world.

Before God she placed her trust in the man who was her husband but sometimes that trust failed her. Could Thomas force her back into his world? As words flowed from her pen she feared his censorship. At some point he must call halt: she almost wanted him to. There was a kind of agony in living with this accepting outsider whose response to the turmoil of his household and his wife's heart was a considered but seemingly dispassionate, 'so be it'.

They clashed, almost inevitably, over their eldest daughter's marriage. Thomas Fell allowed his children to choose their own path to God as he allowed his wife to choose hers. He could do no other. His daughters followed their mother. He tried to woo young Margaret back to the secure life of the law abiding, church going, landed gentry. He wanted her settled and happy. Moreover he wanted her safety. He found her a husband who could give her affection and protection. He was both astonished and hurt by the vehemence of her reaction.

> ...if we should sell the Truth of God...for a
> fading inheritance...we should lose that
> peace which the whole world cannot
> purchase for us.

With the marriage settlement she seemed to reject his paternal love. Thomas would force nothing on her. He walked away to struggle alone with the doubts and questions of the perpetual seeker trying not to give way to the despair of loneliness. Margaret saw the pain beneath the set expression of Thomas's face and averted her eyes.

In the lined face of the father she saw that of the son. Thomas needed the boy now for all his insistence that he complete his legal studies. George was eighteen, nearly nineteen, more child than man, and too easily persuaded into mischief. If he brawled or drank or chased after women it was to impress the reprobates which he claimed as comrades. She urged London-bound Friends to visit him and bring her news. The news she longed for was of his return to the fold. Once he had almost accepted her truth. Let him do so again. Margaret poured out her love and her prayers in letters.

> My dear one, I cannot forget thee; my cries to
> my Heavenly Father are for thee that thou
> may be kept and that the measure of Him in
> thee may be preserved...

At Swarthmoor she lavished the attention she could not give George on his one-time companion, Will Caton. He 'was as tender of me, as if I had been one of her own children' he wrote in his account of his brief life. To him, Margaret wrote,

> My dear Lamb, my dear Love and Life flows
> freely unto thee, who art a vessel fitted for the
> Master's use, and a Babe of the immortal
> Seed, and of the Royal Priesthood, and of the
> True Tabernacle which the Lord pitched and
> not man.

The hyperbole was born of sectarian fervour: the love was real. Thomas never understood the extravagance of its expression. He was a rational man who explained his actions in more measured words.

The godly magistrate would not persecute any man for conscience sake. If he was 'serviceable to Friends' it was because such service matched his own concept of right. The freedom to act as he did was the fruit of worldly power and success that made it unnecessary to pander to those who held sway in London. Thomas rarely went to the capital now, even at Cromwell's bidding. The demise of the revolution that had fired his youth could be watched from afar. He was sure that it was dying. Cromwell's appointment of major generals to govern the English shires was an uncomfortable reminder of military rule. The glimmer of hope, that was the promise of liberty of conscience included in the Instrument of Government, was quenched by the Quaker Act of 1655 and the 'authorised' persecution that was James Nayler's trial and sentencing by Parliament in the following year. Thomas Fell could only grieve for the Parliament that treated the Quaker thus. Barbarity, even officially sanctioned barbarity, had no place in his moral code. Changes to the statute book reflected the nation's intolerance. It became more difficult to keep those who would publish God's truth free of laws that would silence them. Thomas Fell did not stop trying.

> Judge Fell was very serviceable in his day and
> time, to stop the edge of the priests, justices
> and rude multitude, who often fell upon
> Friends, beat them and persecuted them.

Thomas Fell, husband and father, wanted to understand the family he loved: Thomas Fell, seeker, longed to know God. He went less often to St Mary's: William Lampit could no longer claim him as a patron. Now he sat alone in his study, his bible open before him.

> Ye have not chosen me, but I have chosen
> you...If the world hate you, ye know that it
> hated me before it hated you...because ye are
> not of the world, but I have chosen you out of
> the world, therefore the world hateth you...

Thomas wrestled with the text and he wrestled with its expression in this time and this place. He thought of his elder daughters, Margaret, Bridget, Isabel, children no longer. Had faith denied them the joys of youth? He wanted his house to ring with their laughter, not their religious fervour. He wanted to stand by their sides at times of celebration, not between them and their persecutors. He wanted them restored to him, as he wanted their mother.

Margaret Fell keeps her meeting in Swarthmoor's great hall and Thomas sits alone, his study door ajar. That is what legend tells us. He has not yet reached his sixtieth birthday but this is the seventeenth century and he is an old man, laid low by winter illness and ready to admit the afflictions of age. He is used to the loneliness of his family life: he can no longer bear the pain of his soul's homelessness. He hears the woman he loves at prayer: the ardour in her voice is not for him. He fights back the pangs of sexual jealousy. It no longer matters. Thomas struggles to let go of pride in this world's honours: land, riches, office, authority. It is not enough. He confesses his need to analyse and dissect the things of God as if they were the finer points of law. He will not give up reason easily. He clings more tightly still to the solitary nature of his spirit's journey. The seeker holds fast to the quest that has become his purpose. There can be no homecoming until the meeting with God that is death. Judge Fell waits, secure in nothing but his own mortality.

> He Liv'd about six Years after I was convinc'd; in which time it pleas'd the Lord to visit him with Sickness, wherein he became more than usually loving and kind to our Friends call'd Quakers, having been a merciful Man to the Lord's People. I, and many other Friends were well satisfy'd the Lord in mercy receiv'd him to himself. It was in the beginning of the 8th Month, 1658, that he died being about sixty years of age.

He was buried by torchlight in the parish church of St Mary's as befitted a man of his rank and stature.

Oliver Cromwell died in the same year and was buried in Westminster Abbey 'amongst kings and with a more than regal solemnity'.

* * * * *

> Jesus saith unto her, Go, call thy husband,
> and come hither. The woman answered and
> said, I have no husband.

Margaret Fell keeps her Meeting at Swarthmoor still, alone but not alone, seeking the spirit of the man whose wife she had been, whose widow she was. How do you open a marriage to God? He was a good husband, a good father, a good man. The words drummed in her head. Good day, good morrow, good Thomas. Were grief and idiocy one? She realised she was dry-eyed. Those who don't cry take a long time to heal. Had her mother said that, or a nursemaid long ago? Instinctively she put her arms around the daughters who sat closest to her: Sarah sniffed; Bridget's head remained bowed, her thoughts her own. Margaret thought of Rachel, barely five. Would she remember her father? This was a house of women. Her son George was in London again. Thomas had left the law student his books. Was that a judgement on his profligacy?

Margaret struggled to still a wayward mind. She must surrender grief to God, self to silence. Her heart chased its own images. The figure on horseback crossing the Sands. The noise of his returning. The way his voice seemed to echo round the stable yard. The feel of his skin, smooth hands under his riding gloves, the smell of leather and man. She could give this shadow husband back to God. Did she want to probe the pain of marriage? The past forced its way to the surface of her mind. A nervous young bride danced a formal dance of manners with the man of affairs. A woman newly risen from child-bed fought his invasion of her body's healing and rejected his possession of her. Had she been a prisoner in the judge's house and his life? She had not always thought so. How had she lost touch with the joy? For joy there was, and sometimes contentment, and love, and the children. Once she and Thomas had walked in Eden; the gravity of his smile had provoked her mirth; and beneath the laughter she had wanted him with an intensity that racked the whole of her being. Now the solemn-faced husband was dead and the merry young woman laughed no more. The widow ached with the pain of the past, with the emptiness of life as it had been without God. She retched on the bitterness of long ago resentments and wept: the tears did not come easily. She shed them for the man whose life had ended, and she shed them for herself.

Thomas had been a 'tender, loving husband, the kind friend to Friends'. The Lord, in his mercy, had received him to himself. He had not found faith, but God had found purpose for his life. Margaret stood alone before God and found the freedom that is the abandonment of self. In prayer she knew the source of all strength, all courage, all compassion: she knew the love of an undivided heart.

* * * * *

Ulverston 1659: Mistress Fell is lady of the manor and its lord too. The judge has been dead for a year. The town loves him in death as it feared him in life. He remembered its poor in his will and left money for the foundation of a grammar school. He knew where he belonged despite his city ways. The son is still in London. Rumour has him a wastrel, or the victim of his mother's religious excess. Did the lad stand a chance against the Devil's own hysterical outpourings, or whatever now went on at the hall? Ulverston doubted it. The widow keeps court to a motley crew of strangers. Preachers, or beggars and thieves? Friends or lovers? They say she is setting her cap at their leader, George Fox. If she is, it is nothing new. The judge's compliance was the occasion for enough street corner ribaldry in his lifetime.

England 1659: Richard Cromwell is Lord Protector, poor weak Dick. Old Oliver refused the crown but he chose his own son to succeed him.

> About this time great stirs were in the nation,
> the minds of people being unsettled. Much
> plotting and contriving there was by several
> factions…

The plotting started in Westminster. Richard Cromwell received no support from men who had once served his father. The army might have saved him, but its officers were owed arrears of pay and would strike no bargain. Richard took himself into exile leaving England to be governed by the forty-two surviving members of the Rump of the Long Parliament of 1640, hardly a freely elected, representative body. In the absence of authority anyone might make a bid for power.

And God's kingdom, might it come now to an England without Protector or King? The people of God called Quakers waited and watched and prayed. Twenty thousand hearts were opened to the Light of God. Twenty thousand lives were stripped of cumber. Twenty thousand women and men lived with constant attention to the process of revelation that allowed them to discern the will of God. They had no fear of governments. Theirs was the radical voice of 1659, the voice that made middle England tremble. The expression of their radicalism was their opposition to the church tithe. Tithes were an anomaly in a country that had no state church but they remained a powerful symbol of traditional authority. In June the counties of Westmoreland, Cumberland, Lancashire and Cheshire petitioned for their abolition. The petition bore fifteen thousand signatures. In July seven thousand Quaker women made their plea against the same oppression. For a moment it looked as if the old order might give way and forfeit the church tax. It was the sign of resurgent radicalism that General Monk had been waiting for. He marched his army of Restoration south from Scotland. His troopers, interpreting prayer as political conspiracy, broke up the Quaker Meetings. Life did not change for this 'peculiar people'.

* * * * *

> 29th May 1660: This day came in his Majestie
> Charles 2d to London after a sad and long
> Exile, and Calamitous Suffering both of the
> King and Church....

Maypoles reappear on village greens: Jack and Jane rejoice. In the capital men exact ritual vengeance. The bodies of Cromwell, Ireton and Bradshaw are exhumed, 'hanged' at Tyburn and decapitated. The heads are displayed on pikes on Westminster Bridge. Behind closed doors statesmen and councillors negotiate a settlement. The Act of Indemnity and Oblivion forgives those whose deaths have no symbolic value. The New Model Army is disbanded. The English have no love of the soldiery and no inclination to pay their wages. Few limitations are placed on the royal prerogative. Parliament will try to manage the second Charles Stuart as it did the first, by keeping him short of money. The King, restored, is head of the English church.

From exile Charles issues the conciliatory Declaration of Breda promising 'liberty to tender consciences'. His parliament will have none of this, seeing an alliance between church and gentry, between the rectory and the manor, as the logical defence against radicalism in both religion and politics. Anglicanism was not destroyed by the revolution: it has only to come out of hiding. The new king has no strong faith, nor any real interest in religion. Charles is the monarch in a mask out to woo his people. Parliament will not have the non-conforming nation wooed. MPs legislate against dissent: the Act of Uniformity, the Corporation Act, the revised prayer book, the Act Against Quakers, the first and second Conventicle Acts, the Five Mile Act.

Charles, intrigued by the steadfast faith of people the like of whom he has not met in exile, and not a little flattered by their attentions, grants almost random pardons and indulgences. There is no indulgence when the King needs money from his Parliament. The Dutch War proves expensive: the prisons remain full. A pension from the French king gives Charles independence of a kind. In secret, he promises to declare for Rome and Catholicism, but not yet. English dissenters are released from jail. Neither the king nor his privy council wants to provoke trouble at home while they fight a second Dutch War. Parliament and JPs play games with the king. Arrests follow hard on the heels of pardon. England's gentry are in no mood for toleration. Each disturbance, or suspected disturbance, raises the spectre of revolution: the Fifth Monarchy Rising, the Kaber Rigg Plot, the Popish Plot, the Rye House Plot. Religious minorities pose a threat: religious minorities are made to suffer. Not all uncertainty is political: bad harvests, plague and fire threaten even the most conformist of lives.

1660: The King came into his own. For breaching the King's peace or God's, George Fox was arrested at Swarthmoor. The Ulverston constables suspected the Devil's work. Fifteen or sixteen men were set on guard overnight, 'some of whom sat in the chimney for fear I should go up it'. Early next morning Fox was bundled unceremoniously through the town towards Lancaster and prison. Margaret recognised some of the rabble urging the constables on, men who plied trades in Ulverston or worked the land, who counted themselves good Christians and brought up their children in fear of the Lord. She could not see what drove them. Anger and righteousness threatened to overwhelm her. She had no understanding of suspicion that needed the false courage of the mob to give it voice. Resolutely Fox made his act of witness and turned the other cheek: his tormentors were ignorant of his intention. They continued to exchange the ribald comments of those secure in their majority. A newcomer appeared leading Fox's horse. Blows and comments stuttered to a halt. The party prepared to cross the Sands. Mounted, Fox became a man not a victim. The crowd quieted. What happened next was not their concern. In twos and threes they drifted away. Margaret was left alone with her own powerlessness. The man she wanted was Thomas.

* * * * *

And I having a great family, and he being
taken in my house, I was moved of the Lord
to go to the King at Whitehall; and took with
me a declaration, and an information of our
principles, and a long time, and much ado I
had, to get to him.

The woman…went her way into the city …

For God's sake, or George Fox's, Margaret was compelled to travel
south, towards an England that had been part of the judge's life but
was never part of hers. What did she know of the king or his court?
What did she know of the capital with its beggars and rogues, its
honest men and its tricksters? What did she know of masquerade as
she struggled to see herself reflected in the harsh, unyielding light of
God? Innocence was her protection.

A north-country gentlewoman set out for London. She took her
eldest daughter to be her companion. She travelled with Friends. It
was the first journey and it was all the journeys. There was danger
and little comfort, save that which came from companionship.
Horseback was faster than carriage along narrow roads, pitted with
ruts. From Swarthmoor, the party struck out across the treacherous
familiarity of the sands. Sea birds swooping after rotting fish, the
children of fisher folk at play in the shallows. Lancaster: the castle's
dark silhouette rose forbiddingly on its hilltop, Fox's prison. Soldiers
on the move, a raggle-taggle band clinging to some remnant of
military discipline.

The travellers crossed the flat valley of the Lune through pasture-
land where cattle grazed. A horse cast a shoe. They stopped at a
village smithy. The people paid due deference to the sable that
bordered Margaret's cloak. She was unnoticing, intent on her
purpose. A coach passed. The road ahead was deserted: nothing
stirred. The hills of a strange country rose before the travellers.
Sheep dotted the landscape. Rain fell, striking a summer chill. A man
on foot, shepherd or labourer, trudged stoically homewards. One

night was spent with Friends, another at an indifferent inn, where the landlord greeted the King's return with fatalistic gloom. They came south to Leicester. The country was gentler now. The road filled: beggar and thief, priest and peddler, the seller of tracts and the purveyor of baubles and ribbons. The party passed through towns, alive with the noise of market, and through villages that were Sabbath day quiet. Outside a wayside inn an old man snorted in his sleep: somewhere a baby cried. At St Albans the road was thronged with noise and movement: the air thick with the dust of carriage wheels and horses' hooves. A farmer, with no notion of other men's haste, drove his plodding cows home for milking. Too weary now to be excited by novelty, Margaret and her companions had their first sight of London's huddled mass. The merchant's temple, the three brass balls of the pawnbroker's shop, the kerb-side that was the poor man's mansion, the royal palace of Whitehall.

Come buy, come buy. The tarnished glory of Oxford Street. Berwick Street market alive with colour. Carefully, I choose two mangoes, trophies from a warmer clime.

Come enjoy, come enjoy. The juggler on Bankside plays with fire. Outside the National Theatre a French magician tosses an imaginary 'carrotte' to a delighted child.

A pleasure boat charts the black waters of the Thames: a thousand years of history in a two-hour cruise.

At the top of the steps to the Hungerford Bridge a beggar sits, dull grey skin, the stubble of beard, eyes unseeing, vacant.

The soldiers on duty at Horseguards Parade stare into the middle distance. Behind them, in Whitehall, the cumbersome machinery of modern government plods forward.

Access to the King was possible for those prepared to wait on the dictates of court etiquette and royal whim. Charles wanted the love as well as the loyalty of the nation that had executed his father. Margaret waited. She would have the release of George Fox from

Lancaster jail; she would preach truth to her King. She had no fear. Charles Stuart was but a man, albeit a man clad in velvet and lace and the mask of kingship.

How do you touch the hearts of kings? Margaret was cast in the role of honesty in a courtly masque of intrigue and innuendo. She held to the power of God to change lives and worlds. There would be a new heaven and a new earth. The 'Declaration and Information' she presented to the king was her truth, a truth she would speak to the world and by which the world would be convinced. She condemned the persecutors of those who suffered for 'conscience sake'; she condemned the hireling priests and the collection of tithes. She proclaimed the simplicity of a life lived in Christ, where men and women dealt with one another in ways that were not coloured by the masks they wore. This simplicity, this purity, did not need false honours and titles. It did not need oaths. It needed only love and faith. Margaret held fast to the love of Jesus the teacher, the Christ within.

> No People can retain God in their knowl-
> edge, and worship him as God, but first they
> must come to that of God in them...

How do you touch the hearts of kings? The man Margaret petitioned sat insecurely on his throne. Beneath the mask lay fear, suspicion and uncertainty. This nation welcomed him home with fanfares and trumpets, with feasting and celebration: only eleven years had passed since this same nation led his father to the scaffold. Does loyalty change the minds of kings? The 'Declaration and Information' was addressed to the lawmakers, the king and Parliament who framed the statutes that made persecution possible and ultimately had the power to stop it.

> Treason, Treachery and false Dealing we do
> utterly deny, false Dealing, Surmizing, or
> Plotting against any Creature upon the face of
> the of the Earth, and [we] speak the Truth in
> plainness and singleness of heart, and all our
> desire is your Good, and Peace, and Love.

In search of Margaret Fell

She would have Charles respond to the power of God in her words, in her heart and in himself. She would have him understand that the people of God called Quakers were a peaceable people who would not use the world's weapons to establish God's kingdom. The New Jerusalem would not be built with swords.

Margaret waited, sure of God's will.

Sure, but never completely free from doubt, nor from the sense of playing a part on a foreign stage. What place had the widow of one north-country squire, the daughter of another, in this rabbit warren of a palace where the rich, or richly dressed, scampered from room to room in the pursuit of power or pleasure? Margaret stood her ground. God had sent her here for His own purpose. She caught sight of the arrogant, bejewelled beauty of Barbara Villiers, Lady Castlemaine, soon to become the royal mistress, if she was not already. Rumour was rife, but unsure. Before Margaret's uncaring eyes James, Duke of York, paraded Anne Hyde, the Chancellor's daughter. By the end of the year she would be carrying his child and he would marry her. Neither monarch nor nation would celebrate. Mistress or bride, Anne remained a commoner. Who was Margaret Fell amongst so much powder and paint, but an unknown, faceless woman clad in the dull, provincial black of her widowhood? Truth and honesty walked proudly, but they walked in the guise of the petitioner.

As long as George Fox remained in jail Margaret could do nothing but remain in the capital. If she could get no audience with the king, she poured words on to paper, to Charles, to the Duke of York, to their sister the Queen of Bohemia, to the Dowager Henrietta Maria, Charles I's widow. She did not, could not, heed her daughters' urgings that she return home. She sent her love, her advice and her regrets. She would not travel north until Fox was free. The pivot of her life had changed. She had no choice but to witness to her faith, to her love of God and her love for His prophet.

She waited, her hopes crushed both by the king's indifference and his graciousness. What use his charm, if he did nothing? In the end it was to Charles' gallantry that Fox owed his release. It was not Margaret's pleas the king yielded to, but those of Ann Curtis, whose father had been hanged for his loyalty to the first Charles Stuart. The second Charles had few supporters to reward: he bestowed a royal favour on Robert Yeaman's daughter. Fox's freedom came in the manner of kings rather than that of Friends. The world had not changed.

The order for George Fox's release from Lancaster came in September. He was summoned to London to appear before the King's Bench. By October he was a free man.

God freed James Nayler that autumn. Released from jail, broken in body, belatedly and grudgingly forgiven by Fox, he left London for the north and home. At a Huntingdon roadside he collapsed.

> There is a spirit which I feel that delights to
> do no evil nor to revenge any wrong...I
> found it alone, being forsaken.

Margaret could not bring herself to leave the capital. The city, for all its stench and noise, its crowds, its waste and its deprivation, claimed a part of her. Somewhere within this maze of streets, lived George Fell, student at Grays Inn. They'd met, mother and son, during the last months, brief unsatisfactory visits in which nothing real was said. Sensing his unhappiness, she had tried not to judge him; but there were the debts, the shadows under his eyes and the pallor of his skin. Despair disguised as bravado made her heart ache. She hadn't been able to hold her silence, but it was too late for mother love. In the background was Hannah Potter, widow. At the year's end George married her: his mother fought down the nagging pains of jealousy and the feeling that her son deserved something more than second-chance affection. Moreover, it was marriage with the world. Condemnation was too easy. She tried to hold the couple in prayer.

She was done with this city now. She longed for the comfort of the familiar, for the hills and their mists, for the grey expanse of sand that was Morecambe Bay, for her home and hearth and the people who cared for her. She would have ridden north in the new year, despite the winter cold, but events contrived to keep her in London.

> ...the Fifth-Monarchy-Men raised an
> Insurrection and Tumult in the City of
> London, and then all our Meetings were
> disturb'd, and Friends taken up ...

In January 1661 the Fifth Monarchy Men rebelled. At their head Thomas Venner, convinced that he knew God's will, preached the book of Daniel and the imminent rule of the Saints. The government was more easily convinced of the imminence of national rebellion. Fourteen ineffectual revolutionaries were executed and their heads displayed on Tower Bridge. In the panic that followed all those who dissented in matters of religion were suspected of treason. Across the country five thousand Quakers were cast into jail: it was summary imprisonment without warrant, charge or trial. Margaret stayed in London to plead for them.

> On 24th, at Swarthmore, forty three Persons
> were taken, some out of their houses, others
> from the Market, and some from their Labour
> and Employment, by a party of Horsemen,
> and without any Warrant, Mittimus, or
> Examination before a Magistrate, committed to
> Lancaster Castle...

Men who languished in jail could not sow spring corn. Bridget Fell wrote to her mother,

> ...if the things continue that they keep men
> in custody that should till the ground, the
> time of seeding being now, it cannot be
> expected that we should be able to maintain
> them in prison, hire our tillage at home, and
> pay that which will be requested of us long.

There was no public outcry. The forty-three innocents going about their daily lives were tomorrow's revolutionaries. Ulverston would sleep more soundly with them safe behind bars. The nation endorsed the government's fears. Margaret continued to petition the king, who made ready promises with little thought of the difficulty of keeping them. Fox, only too aware of the extent of the danger, hastened to declare his pacifism and his loyalty to the crown.

> Our principle is, and our practices have always
> been, to seek peace and ensue it; to follow after
> righteousness and the knowledge of God;
> seeking the good and welfare, and doing that
> which tends to the peace of all.

'To seek peace and ensue it' was a noble aspiration but when were governments ever moved by noble sentiments? What moved Charles' Privy Council was an increasing awareness of its own folly. House-searches, arrests and imprisonment on this scale threatened, rather than secured, national stability. Charles swayed with the wind and issued a general order for the release of Friends. His justices kept their leaders prisoner. The pattern for the reign was set.

White for hope, red for remembrance: I take the two poppies, one white, one red, and twist their stems together. It's a very small gesture, a penny-worth of prayer for peace.

I suddenly hear again the voice of Sima, talking about his work with traumatised children in war-torn Sierra Leone. His intensity hurts.

'Hope for the future is the only bit of joy you can give a weeping child.'

I am back in Birmingham, last year. The city celebrates, Halloween, Guy Fawkes, Diwali: for weeks the night echoes with the sound of fireworks. Sima's black face is grey, he starts and shakes. At last, the celebrations cease.

I breathe his relief: I do not have to do his returning.

* * * * *

Margaret 'had Freedom in Spirit to return Home to visit my Children and Family'.

The journey north was long and wearisome. The midland shires had seen heavy rain: the horses picked their way along pot-holed tracks. It was September: the days were shortening. Country inns offered rough comfort. Harvest was all but over, the countryside settling into the brown-green of autumn. At dusk they crossed into Furness. Swarthmoor was lit by rush light and candle. Homecoming was the clatter of hooves on stone, shouted greetings, orders given about luggage, the sudden warmth of the house, the smell of food. Welcome was the hand that took her cloak, the voice that exclaimed at the mud on its hem; was quiet concern that she felt tired or chilled. It was the ebullience of Susannah and Rachel, and the strain on Bridget's weary face.

Margaret could not evade the responsibility. She had not been here to answer the constable's knock at her door. It was Bridget, already beset by ill health, who took charge, who offered comfort and reassurance where it was needed. It was Bridget who made decisions in the face of winter hunger and winter shortages. It was Bridget who answered the rumours and suspicion that surrounded her mother's continued absence.

They sit at table together, mother and daughters, the silence broken by Bridget's wearisome clearing of her throat. Margaret is irritated, then ashamed, conscious of her debt to this daughter. The meal is served. She fights back the urge to rebuke the slowness of a maid she does not recognise. Bridget feels the reproof in the air. She imagines criticism of scant portions and bread that is already two days old. Young Margaret tries to talk of London, Friends, the king and his court. She gets little response. For over a year she has been her mother's confidant and companion. Now she feels locked out of the older woman's thoughts. She looks at her sister; the weight of her burden makes her own position seem privileged. She reaches for Bridget's hand. It is not offered, but neither is it withdrawn.

Margaret sees the gesture and bends forward to kiss them both. It is an uneasy truce. She would always claim authority in this house, but she would always have work to do elsewhere. She would always need the help of one of her daughters, but they must be free to walk their own paths.

She rejoiced in their happiness as they fell in love and were loved in return. She rejoiced that the men they loved were Friends. And she felt the sadness of parting. John Rous would take young Margaret to the West Indies but, first, the couple would be married in her house among Friends. It was what she wanted for all of her children. Twice in 1662, Friends met in Swarthmoor's great hall to bear witness to a marriage. In January, Margaret Fell the younger married John Rous of Barbados, and in March, Bridget Fell married John Draper of county Durham.

> ...then as they are moved of the Lord, by his power and in his fear, they may take each other in the Meeting & speak what the unlimited power and spirit gives utterance.

Margaret sees God at work in the hearts of her daughters and is overwhelmed by a sense of His goodness as they offer their lives and their marriages to Him. God is their strength. His is the love that will allow them to live faithfully. She sees the danger they face in the way ahead. Their paths will never be smooth: the times are too treacherous. The meeting gathers in prayer around them. God blesses these unions. In the silence there is solemnity, love, and tears. There is celebration in the midst of suffering.

The guests have gone. Bride and groom have set out on their journey. In the hearth a log cracks open. A floorboard creaks. Margaret sits heavily on the wooden settle, giving way to weariness. She relives the day, letting moments come and go. How Isabel had fussed about the hang of Bridget's gown. The boyish pride with which John Draper looked at his bride across the meeting and his nervous smile. Her daughter had looked well, at peace, content. She was over last winter's sickness but she was not strong. Let God protect her and comfort her. She remembers Bridget aged nine or ten, suddenly maternal, struggling to carry the wriggling bundle that was Sarah at two. They had fallen at her feet in a kicking, squealing mass of limbs and petticoats. Thomas stood in the doorway unable to contain his laughter. Who shares her memories now?

We sit over our teacups, you and I, saying little, making vague plans for the day. Outside the window the ring doves flutter furiously in the first rush of courtship. We have left all that behind us: we carry it with us still.

* * * * *

>...and then I was moved of the Lord to go to London again, not knowing what might be the Matter or Business that I should go for. And when I came to Warrington, in my way to London, I met with an Act of Parliament, made against the Quakers for refusing Oaths.
>
>At this time Friends Meetings in London were much troubled with Soldiers, pulling Friends out of their Meetings, and beating them with their Muskets and Swords; ...many were cast into Prison, through which many lost their Lives; and all this being done to a peaceable People, only for Worshipping God, as they in Conscience were perswaded...

In the summer of 1662 Margaret returned to the capital. It was the year in which Charles married Catherine of Braganza, his Portuguese princess. Poor barren Catherine! Her husband tarried awhile to admire her fine eyes and then fathered fourteen illegitimate children on other women.

King Charles was now head of an English church that was established by law. His parliament passed the Act of Uniformity and on 24th August, the feast of St Bartholomew, the king bade his ministers of religion demonstrate their loyalty by conducting morning service from the revised prayer book. For the most part they complied. Only a tenth of England's clergy turned their back on restored Anglicanism. Among them was William Lampit, priest of Ulverston.

The Quaker Act was passed in the same year by a Parliament intent on magnifying sectarian dangers in the wake of the Fifth Monarchy Rebellion. The Friend who refused to swear an oath was now a criminal. More significantly, so was the Friend who left his house to meet with more than four others 'under pretence of worship not authorised by law'. The penalty for a first offence was a fine: for the third it was transportation.

A woman plainly dressed in country-cut black, a humble petitioner at a royal court, again addressed a king from the depths of her heart and her soul. The passion with which she talked, the fire in her eyes as well as her voice, once more amused a man of little faith who habitually charmed women. Charles made promises of indulgence or pardon that were strangely out of keeping with the uncompromising mood of Parliament and nation.

Outside his palace walls militia men burst into silent meetings.

> On the 28th of October the Meetings were again violently broke up by Soldiers, and that Day were committed to Newgate, from the Meeting at the Bull and Mouth, eighty Persons: From the Peel in John's-street, one Hundred and twenty eight...

Swords and muskets: the world's defence against prayer.

> ...I say unto you, That ye resist not evil: but whosoever shall smite thee on thy right cheek, turn to him the other also.

It was bleak winter, no matter the changing seasons. Bridget Draper died in childbirth. Margaret braved the winter roads to be with her. She could only watch her daughter struggle, and cease to struggle. She willed God not to let this birth be a death as well, but prayer and love and hope were not enough. At the last she knew Bridget to be safe in God's keeping, but what help was that to the feeble infant whimpering in his grandmother's arms? They named the baby Isaac. He did not survive. On a sugar plantation in distant Barbados young Margaret Rous, pregnant with her first child, fell from a horse and miscarried. Her mother could offer no comfort: she did not know.

A woman listens to the prayer that is the voice of silence. She hears the words of Christ in her own heart. Understanding is her gift from God.

> Let Faith, Hope and Charity (which remains) be the Crown and Desire of your Souls, which suffereth all things, beareth all things, hopeth all things, believeth all things, and endureth all things; this will preserve you indeed: This will keep you low, and sensible, and seasoned, and will sanctifie your Hearts, and purifie your Minds; so that you will not value nor care what Man can do unto you, who is but a Vapour; but the Everlasting Inheritance (which is not of this World) you will come to receive: For it is your Father's good pleasure to give you a Kingdom...

May 1663: The days are lengthening: the season mild. Travellers set out from Swarthmoor: Margaret, her daughters Sarah and Mary, Leonard Fell, Thomas Salthouse. They are well mounted: this is no short journey. South to Bristol: tall ships in the Channel, crowded streets, the disconsolate stares of press-ganged farmers' sons. Somerset's orchards and pasture-land. West into Devon and Cornwall, tin mines, the bent figures of home-going miners, surf breaking on a deserted beach, fishing villages, the trumpet call of Fox's preaching. Bristol again, the spectre of the gallows, the bold eyes of a harlot, carriages, wealth. North once more, the Derbyshire peaks. Fox, met again at Balby, the Light of God in his servant.

Through Yorkshire, Durham, Northumberland, Westmoreland ...
The horses disturb the dust of a dry August.

> I was moved of the Lord again to travel into
> the Countries to visit Friends...it was thought
> we Travelled about a Thousand Miles.

Meals shared in farmhouse kitchens. Veined hands breaking flat black bread. News. Sorrow and joy, laughter and tears. Prayer, the constant prayer of a gathered people. Endurance etched as pain on one face, on another, worn as quiet steadfastness. Faithfulness. Love, in each hand and voice that bids the travellers welcome. Love, in the sudden smile of a child and the cracked tones of age. Courage, to defy the magistrates and the neighbours who used to be friends, to condemn the empty forms that prevail in the steeple houses, the worship that is no worship, the oppression and injustice of the lawmakers. Courage to bear witness to a better way. And above all unity and fellowship, the 'oneness' in which lay this people's strength under God.

The mood of the country was bitter. Cromwell's republic was a slice of history the nation would rather not own. The Kaber Rigg Plot was no revolution, just a vain attempt to force liberty of conscience on king and government from remote Westmoreland. In its aftermath intolerance spread. Difference invited persecution. The Furness magistrates had no love for Thomas Fell's memory, nor sympathy for his widow with her outlandish beliefs. Richard and William Kirkby were local men, their cousin, Daniel Fleming, lived at Rydal Mount by Ambleside. They shared Royalist politics and a desire to rid the north west of the Quaker curse.

George Fox was at Swarthmoor that winter. The hall became the focus of their plotting. They would take two birds with a single shot if they could. Fox feared no earthly magistrates. He confronted them in person, declaring his loyalty and that of the peaceable people of God called Quakers. Margaret wrote to Richard Kirkby with all the arguments she had presented to the king.

> ...we are no such people as are any way ill affected to either our King, State or Government, or to any man or person upon the Earth, but we desire the good, and the peace of all men, and that under this Government we might live a godly and peaceable life...

Words changed no minds. The magistrates would enforce the Quaker Act. They would break up the Quaker conspiracy.

George Fox was their first quarry. In January 1664 he appeared at Lancaster sessions. The magistrates had a ready trap to spring upon the Quaker. They tendered him the Oath of Allegiance. Fox would not, could not swear. He was not disloyal to the King: he simply did not recognise a double standard. 'Swear not at all', was the demand of God made in Scripture. The court recognised only the demands of the law. Fox was jailed until the March assizes. Margaret waited: they surely would not leave her at liberty.

From Lancaster Daniel Fleming wrote to Secretary Williamson in London,

> I gave you an account in my last of our proceedings against the Quakers at Lancaster and Kendall, and notwithstanding the same, Mrs Fell (Oliver's Judge Fell's widdow, & now wife or I know not what to Geo Fox) had a greater meeting of them at her house then ever, the very next Sunday after the Sessions, on purpose as tis generally thought to affront our authority ... If we receive any encouragement from you herein, wee'l tender her the oath, and so praemunire her according to Law, which will be the only way to take effectuall course with her, who is the chiefe maintainer of that party in this Country.

18th February 1664: Margaret Fell is summoned before Daniel Fleming and his fellow justices in their chambers at Ulverston. Fleming, irate, determined to snare his quarry, demands that Margaret hold no more Quaker meetings at her house. Her refusal is adamant. God's servant looks at the magistrate with all the disdain of the great lady for the upstart. Daniel Fleming is no upstart. He will humble her. If she is the king's loyal subject she must prove her loyalty. She must swear the oath. Slowly, in the tones of a parent instructing a child, she repeats the words of the Gospel,

> Swear not at all; neither by heaven; for it is
> God's throne: nor by the earth; for it is his
> footstool: neither by Jerusalem; for it is the
> city of the great King. Neither shalt thou
> swear by thy head, because thou canst not
> make one hair white or black. But let your
> communication be, Yea, yea; Nay, nay: for
> whatsoever is more than these cometh of evil.

Her righteousness grates on his nerves. If only she would plead or beg mercy…If she were not a woman…He clenches his fist, then almost forces the muscles to relax. Mistress Fell is but a prisoner, a common felon. He does not look at her again. Brusquely, he orders the constable escort her across the Sands to await trial. Margaret feels the knot tighten in her stomach. She will show no fear. As she makes to follow her escort, her head is high.

Before her she sees the grim silhouette of Lancaster Castle. Somewhere in its depths George Fox is a prisoner. As she crosses the Sands the thought gives her no comfort. She is alone and she is afraid. She struggles with a self who will not, cannot offer the fear to God. In Him lies her strength. His light is her armour.

* * * * *

March 14th 1664. The courtroom of Lancaster Castle. Judge Fell's widow enters, her daughters clustered about her, Isabel, Sarah, Susannah and Rachel, three young women sharing their mother's faith and determination and a child who scarce understands the full implications of the proceedings. They appear at once vulnerable and formidable. The prisoner in the dock, powerless against her persecutors, has contrived to set the stage.

Mistress Fell will have the judge remember her children's father, just as she will have him remember that she has no husband to protect her. Judge Twisden remembers. All courtesy and concern, he has them seated. Good manners cannot long disguise the real business of the court. The charge is read.

In holding Quaker meetings in her home at Swarthmoor Margaret Fell claims the right to worship God in the only way which is possible for her, a way free of the trappings of church and priest, a way which answers the simplicity that is in Christ with the simplicity that is in her own heart. But it is not the law's way. Once more she is ordered to swear the Oath of Allegiance as proof of her loyalty to the crown. Once more she refuses.

Margaret stands in the dock. She commands attention. Judge, lawyer, constable, friend, enemy and idle onlooker alike: all eyes are turned on her. Her gaze does not waver, nor her voice falter.

> ...I am here this Day upon this Account, to bear Testimony to the Truth.

> ...upon the Account of my Conscience, and not for any Evil or Wrong done to any man...

> ...I say I owe Obedience and Allegiance unto Christ Jesus, who commands me not to swear at all...

> ...I must offer and tender my Life, and all for my Testimony, if it be required of me...

Her responses come from God: she makes them to her judges, to George Fox, her fellow prisoner in this fortress jail, to the world and to herself. The act of public witness gives her courage. She does not think about the consequences. She has never wanted for food or shelter, for welcome at a well-laden table, or rest at a warm hearth. Now the constables lead her away to a prison cell.

Judge Twisden is a man of compassion as well as of the law. He offers her freedom in return for her word that no Quaker Meetings will be held at her house.

> I would rather lie where I am; for as I told
> you before, I must keep my Conscience clear,
> for which I suffer…

She lies in her prison cell. First her father's house and then Thomas's sheltered her from foul weather as well as fair. Now rain and wind blow in on her.

In August she appears again at the assize, this time before Judge Turner.

> I am clear and innocent of wronging any
> Man upon the Earth…

The Judge rises to pronounce verdict and sentence. The court is quiet and still.

Right is with the king. Margaret Fell, prisoner at the bar, is praemunire. It is the medieval sentence of outlawry. The judge's widow no longer has the protection of the king's law. She is stripped of rights and status, of wealth and freedom. The king can take possession of her land, her chattels and her home whenever it pleases him to do so. She will remain a prisoner so long as it pleases the king and the king's magistrates. The sentence has denied her a future. God is her only refuge.

> Although I am out of the King's Protection,
> yet I am not out of the protection of the
> Almighty God.

It is a last defiance. She is led away, her head still high, her step sure. The onlookers shuffle to their feet. Slowly the courtroom clears.

In search of Margaret Fell

If I stood accused of being a woman of faith would my accusers find enough evidence to convict me? Do I stand aside from the false values of my time? Does my life bear witness to my truth?

> Who shall separate us from the love of Christ?
> Shall tribulation, or distress, or persecution, or
> famine, or nakedness, or peril, or sword?

Margaret Fell is alone. The court room drama is over. The elation has vanished. Tiredness takes hold of her. She becomes aware of the pain pounding at her temples. Her shoulders stoop. Her pride crumples. She weeps. Once Thomas protected her from this but his spirit cannot rescue her. Had she ever believed it could?

Her gentle birth, her widowhood, her wealth give her protection, even here, but she can neither understand that nor be thankful for it. She is alone, a prisoner without identity or background and she is afraid. She does not expect cruelty or any greater discomfort than she suffered while awaiting trial. She fears the unknown. Her sentence carried no term of years: she is here for as long as it might please the king. She conjures images of home. She pictures herself sitting, working at the scarred wooden surface of her desk, in the hour when daylight turns to dusk, and Rachel rushing in headlong to put her arms around her and deliver herself proudly of some small piece of news. How much of her youngest daughter's growing up will majesty deprive her of?

It is late August. The countrywoman is shut off from the seasons. There is no sun to warm her skin. Here summer is fetid heat, stale air, the taint of food that will not keep. Flies buzz interminably. She sleeps little, then finds she cannot rouse herself. She fights to come to terms with this unending confinement. She will not, cannot, deny her faith but sometimes she would sacrifice anything else in exchange for the freedom to stride across God's hills and breathe His pure air.

There is a cruel monotony to imprisonment. So little changes that there are scarce any decisions to make. There is a pattern of a kind.

Hours are marked, not by monastic bells or the chimes of the clock, but by the comings and goings of the turnkeys. Men, armed with swords and muskets, carrying keys, cloaked with authority, divide the Quaker woman's days. Margaret reaches a kind of acceptance: she has no choice. She becomes almost indifferent to the harshness of her surroundings, to the crude manners and rough voices of those who have the power to bid her 'come' or 'stay'.

Margaret Fell is no hapless victim. She refused to swear the Oath of Allegiance, knowing full well that there would be a price to pay. She must share the suffering that is the lot of the people of God called Quakers that she might be more truly one of them.

> I am present with you, who are obedient to the measure of Eternal Light, which never changes, and who abides in the Oneness of the Spirit, and in the Bond of Peace, which never can be broken, nor taken from you: Here is freedom which the world knows not…

The words are Margaret's own, written a decade ago to other prisoners in this place. They must strengthen her now. Her jailers cannot confine her spirit. Alone in her cell she struggles to hold herself in the light of God that she might discover anew His purpose in her life.

Even in jail she finds fellowship. By the miracle that is the fickleness of authority, the Quaker prisoners are allowed the use of a room within the castle in which they might meet together for worship. Beaten but not defeated, bruised in body or spirit, sick, deprived of physical comfort, worried about the safety of their families, unfailing in their trust in God: they come together. They are one in their pain and their hope. In those first months George Fox is among them. In his leadership they find their inspiration. Prison has not quenched the fire of his words. He still walks proudly before his jailers daring his followers to do likewise. Margaret adds her own words of joy and encouragement.

> So dear Hearts, ye are purged, ye are washed, and cleansed and purified through

> Sufferings...rejoice, inasmuch as ye are made
> Partakers of Christ's Sufferings.

She listens to the stories of men and women who refuse to be defeated. She hears the steadfast conviction in the voices of those whose bodies have been battered by the violence of the mob or the magistrates. She is a part of their suffering.

* * * * *

Margaret is not forgotten by those beyond the prison walls. There are letters and visitors, clean linen, food prepared outside the jail. There is always one of her daughters staying in Lancaster to be near her.

She hears news but she is no longer in touch with events. Once she went boldly to Whitehall to demand that King Charles grant liberty of conscience and worship to the people called Quakers. Now that the pain and anguish caused by senseless persecution are part of her life, she can only write letters. In 1664 Parliament passed the first Conventicle Act. It reinforced the Quaker Act. The intention was the same, the sentences harsher. Fired with anger at the blindness of government, Margaret harangued the king.

> What Laws have you made or changed, save
> such as have laid Oppression and Bondage
> on the Consciences of God's People...? The
> greatest Crime that you could find with the
> People of God was, that they obeyed and wor-
> shipped Christ Jesus,

Charles II did not respond: it was, after all, only a letter from a subject singularly lacking in power or influence. The king must pacify his parliament, bowing to fear and prejudice in exchange for money with which to fight the Dutch.

There are other Friends who go to the royal court, who wait for hours or days for an audience with the king that they might plead for Margaret Fell's release. Her eldest daughter and her husband, Margaret and John Rous, now returned from Barbados, are foremost among them. They try and fail. The king wears the mask of majesty defeated. He has led England into a disastrous war. Within a year his country will be scourged by plague. Within two his capital city will be razed by fire. What is the fate of one woman to him?

The seventeen-year-old Mary Fell visited the Rous's in London. She became ill: it was the winter of 1664 and there were already rumours of plague. Her prisoner mother can do nothing. Accepting her own powerlessness, Margaret does not suffer the physical anxiety that engulfed her as Bridget lay between the life and death of childbirth. She struggles to picture Mary ill and needing her, to think in terms of possets and potions. She has lost touch with the practical, every-day self who would visit, advise and fuss. She prays. It is all that is left her. She feels Mary's 'spirit near and dear and present with me. Whether in body or out, with the Lord and to the Lord of Heaven and earth she is given freely and His heavenly and holy will I freely submit to...'

Margaret let her children go. She could not call halt to their growing, their loving, their falling sick or dying. Mary recovered. Isabel left Swarthmoor for Bristol where she was to marry William Yeamans. Will Caton, onetime companion to the young George Fell and loved as a son by Margaret, died in the winter of 1665, travelling for Truth in the Low Countries, worn out by sufferings at thirty. Rejoicing and mourning: what place did either have in this castle jail? Margaret did not know. She forced herself to think of her own son. Marriage vows and marriage settlements had done nothing to steady him. He still spent too freely, seeking the approval of men of greater rank and status than he. He was weak, too weak to stand by the convictions of either of his parents. Margaret shuddered at the alacrity with which this son of hers had sought a royal pardon for Thomas's republicanism. She could not understand his need for the protective cloak of conformity. Now she was sure Daniel Fleming and the Kirkbys would make easy game of him in their plotting against her.

They wasted no time. A bare six months after Margaret was sentenced George petitioned the king for the Swarthmoor estate, his mother 'being seduced into that Phanatique opinion of the Quakers'. To four of his sisters, Sarah, Mary, Susannah and Rachel, Swarthmoor was home: it was no longer his mother's house. By the sentence of praemunire, which put Margaret outside the law's protection, it became forfeit to the crown. The king's agents did not take possession but the threat was there. George sought to remove the threat by claiming house and land for himself. In January 1665 his petition was granted. His action was almost excusable as a way of securing possession within the Fell family but who could believe in the purity of his motive? Suspicion nagged at his mother. George and Hannah had part of the Marsh Grange estate as their marriage portion. They did not need Swarthmoor too. Would her son have her daughters homeless? When he brought his wife north they seemed content to settle at Marsh Grange. Margaret was relieved. She loved George but she no longer trusted him.

Like all those she loved and didn't see he became a shadow, a memory without form or substance. Once, the authorities, for no apparent reason, allowed her a brief visit home. It was October, bright, cold autumn. She smelt the salt of the Sands: the horses kicked up a chill spray. At the first sight of home tears pricked at her eyelids. It was twenty long months since she was first taken from this house. In the distance a kestrel hovered over an invisible prey. Margaret shivered. What was she but prey to authority's whim? Did they think to weaken her resolve by sending her home? She would not renounce her faith. She would not swear the Oath of Allegiance. She must hold fast to God. Now she hugged Rachel tightly and discovered that her youngest child's head reached her own shoulder. She sat before the fire in her hearth and, in muscles stiffened by confinement and the long ride home, felt the first signs of her body's ageing. She forced herself to take pleasure in simple comforts: this fire, the plentiful food served at her table, her own bed, and her own people. Margaret and John Rous had brought Mary home: she realised how much she had missed her eldest daughter. There was the gentle exchange of domestic news: the Rous's London house described, young Margaret's obvious pregnancy delighted in. There was the fuss of almost too much care and concern. Friends visited: they kept their meeting at Swarthmoor still. Her imprisonment was no defeat. They came to tell her so, to offer their companionship and their love.

It was soon over. She had not ceased to listen for the constable's rap on the door. Yet when the guards came to escort her back across the Sands it was a shock. She accompanied them, riding into the autumn mist, uncomprehending. Why had these few precious days been offered to be snatched back so soon?

Later, they give her leave to attend a Quaker Meeting in Cheshire. It is 1667, the third year of her imprisonment. It is a dream: the prisoner released to worship God. Why then is she a prisoner? Is the law making a jest of her faith, of her life? She walks towards a doorway, looks into a room, sees a sea of faces, sees George Fox. She sits, bewildered, opening herself to the wisdom of God. The meeting gathers. The light of God sears her soul. She sees the signs of her own weakness and failure, and alongside them her courage and steadfastness. Fox speaks in words that echo with the sounds of thunder, fire and victory. His strength under God answers hers. For all she is a woman, his life is the mirror for her own.

* * * * *

Women's Speaking Justified: the title announced her intent. The woman in the prison cell frowns at the page before her as she strives for the right tone. She is God's servant entrusted with His Gospel. To read her words must be to believe. Boldly, she sets down her premise:

> ...Whereas it hath been an objection in the minds of many, and several times hath been objected by the clergy or ministers and others, against womens speaking in the Church. And so consequently (it) may be taken that they are condemned for meddling in the things of God....

She knows it is not so. She has been a wife, helpmeet to a man who could govern her and gainsay her in worldly affairs, but her soul is her own. Before God they were equal.

If claiming the right of speech be meddling, then she would meddle! The women of the Bible close ranks behind her, affirming her, loving her, arming her with their stories. Eve, Sarah, Rachel, Leah, Deborah, Jael, Ruth, Naomi, Mary of Magdala, Mary of Bethany, Martha, Mary the mother of Jesus. With their companionship how can she fail?

Paradise must be her starting point. 'In the image of God created he them, male and female; and God blessed them.' She knew herself blessed of the God who had told Adam and Eve, 'Be fruitful and multiply'. How she had rejoiced in her own fertility! Man and woman, husband and wife, were but two parts of a single whole. 'God hath put no such difference between male and female as men would make.' Yet Eve, beguiled by the wiles of the serpent to eat the fruit that would give her wisdom, was branded a temptress. Were not Adam and Eve equally tempted? Why did the church vilify only Eve? Why should the church condemn women when Christ was born of a woman?

That same church is so often pictured as a woman. Margaret relishes the rich imagery used by David to speak of Christ and His church.

> The King's daughter is all glorious within: her clothing is of wrought gold. She shall be brought unto the king: with gladness and rejoycing shall they be brought; they shall enter into the kings pallace.

God's church, God's all glorious bride.

> And those that speak against the woman's speaking, speak against the Church of Christ and the seed of the woman, which seed is Christ.

Margaret walks the Galilean shore with the women who knew Jesus of Nazareth. Her heart fills with joy and pride for it is to the women that He admits his deity. The woman of Samaria told Jesus,

> 'I know that when the Messiah cometh, (which is called Christ) when he cometh he will tell us all things.' Jesus saith unto her, 'I that speak unto thee am he.'

And to Martha, Jesus said,

> 'I am the resurrection and the life: he that believeth on me, though he were dead, yet shall he live; and whosoever liveth and believeth shall never die. Believest thou this?' She answered, 'Yea Lord, I believe thou art the Christ, the Son of God'.

The women see God in the person of Jesus the teacher, and in them He recognises faithfulness. Was it not a woman who, by anointing her Lord, foretold his Passion? And did He not silence his disciples' criticism of her by saying,

> '...wheresoever this Gospel shall be preached in the whole world, there shall also this that this woman hath done be told, for a memorial of her.'

And he forgave her sins 'for she hath loved much'.

The women of Galilee were driven by love. They stood in the shadow of the cross and wept as the Son of God died.

> And when the Sabbath was past, Mary Magdalene, and Mary the mother of James, and Salome had brought sweet spices that they might anoint him. And very early in the morning, the first day of the week, they came unto the sepulchre at the rising of the sun...

So great was the love of these women that 'they could not depart as the men did, but sat watching and waiting, and weeping about the sepulchre until the time of his resurrection...'

It is Mary Magdalene who Jesus trusted 'to go to my brethren and say unto them I ascend unto my Father and your Father, and to my God and your God'.

Margaret needs no other affirmation. The depth of the love flowing between Jesus and his women disciples is a part of her. It lives in the silence with which she meets God.

She opens her Bible at the first letter to the Corinthians, chapter fourteen. If she is to confound her critics she must unravel the words of the Apostle Paul.

> Let your women keep silence in the Church.

The words are too often quoted out of context, too often used to 'stop the message and word of the Lord God in women, by contemning and despising of them'. To whom did the injunction originally apply? The women of Corinth constrained by their own confusions, by the dictates of the Law, by their own immodesty might rightfully be expected to sit in silence. Nor would Paul have the wife usurp the authority of her husband. She had never usurped Thomas's authority but she chose her own path to God. She has the right to speak of it without let or hindrance, without fear of punishment.

Women of faith will always claim authority in the church. There will always be those who 'have the power and Spirit of the Lord Jesus poured upon them, and have the message of the Lord Jesus given unto them'. Women who given 'the everlasting Gospel to preach' must make themselves heard.

Certainty drove her pen forward. Her nib scoured into the page.

> But all this opposing and gainsaying of women's speaking hath risen out of the bottomless pit and (out of the) spirit of darkness...

It would end, must end, as surely as the false church must fall, the night of the apostasy be over and the true light shine forth.

> And the true light now shines, the morning-light, the bright morning-star, the root and offspring of David. He is risen, he is risen! Glory to the highest for evermore! And the joy of the morning is come…

Margaret shared the joy. The God of light shone in her prison cell.

> …and our holy city, 'the New Jerusalem', is coming down from heaven. And her light will shine throughout the whole earth, even as a 'jasper stone, clear as christal' – which brings freedom and liberty, and perfect redemption to her whole seed. And this is that woman and image of the eternal God that God hath owned, and doth own, and will own for evermore.

Woman, made in the image of God. So many women walked the pages of the Bible, strong in faith, loving and courageous. Their stories were hers, to learn from and to grow from. She could not possibly hope to include them all, but she wanted to celebrate their lives.

> In the time of the Gospel, when Mary came to salute Elizabeth 'in the hill country' in Judea; and when Elizabeth heard the salutation of Mary 'the babe leaped in her womb and she was filled with the Holy Spirit' and Elizabeth spoke with a loud voice, 'Blessed art thou amongst women, blessed is the fruit of thy womb; whence is this to me, that the mother of my Lord should come to me? For lo, as soon as thy salutation came to my ear, the babe leaped in my womb for joy. For blessed is she that believes, for there shall be a performance of those things which were

told her from the Lord.' And this was
Elizabeth's sermon concerning Christ, which
at this day stands upon record. And then
Mary said, 'My soul doth magnifie the Lord,
and my spirit rejoyceth in God my Saviour,
for he hath regarded the low estate of his
hand-maid. For behold, from henceforth all
generations shall call me blessed; for he that
is mighty, hath done to me great things, and
holy is his name.'

Mary and Elizabeth. How their lives preached! They were her
patterns and examples. Across centuries, they spoke to her of love
between women, and of the love of women for God, of His trust in
them and their absolute acceptance of that trust. They answered
God's call without question, or argument, or hesitation as she had
struggled to do in her far humbler fashion. They knew the possibility
of change, of a new beginning, as she knew it now.

He hath scattered the proud in the imagina-
tions of their own hearts. He hath put down
the mighty from their seats and exalted them
of low degree. He hath filled the hungry with
good things, and the rich he hath sent empty
away.

She too lived in a world that could be turned upside down. Would
that the king, his magistrates and his priests could be made to see it!
She had only contempt for the priests who used Mary's song as part
of their 'Common Prayer' but denied women the right to speak in
their churches. Margaret's spirit rejoiced in Mary's words. The
stories of Mary and Elizabeth sang in her heart.

Now here you may see how these two women
prophesied of Christ, and preached better
then all the blind priests did in that age, and
better than this age also, who are beholding
to women to make use of their words.

I claim my right to 'meddle in the things of God', to take a journey through two lives and tell of two women growing into faith. I walk two paths, speak in two voices that I might understand how God lives in both of us. I wrestle with words. I stand before a faded picture of the past and try to breathe life into it. I know the shortcomings of my tale. I endlessly redraft, willing the page to match the image in my mind. I struggle with the solitary nature of the task. The writer spends too much time alone. I come to accept that telling this tale is as much a part of my calling as writing *Women's Speaking Justified* was of Margaret Fell's. We would both celebrate what it is to be a woman before God. We would both be heard.

* * * * *

The turnkey makes his loud, bullying progress through the jail. The wheedling tones of a prostitute, jailed for theft rather than immorality, promise him her body in exchange for little more than a crust of bread. The cruel laughter with which he spurns heaven complete with dirt, vermin and disease echoes through the stone passageways.

Charles, king of this imperfect realm of England, takes his barren queen to Tunbridge Wells that spa water might fill her empty womb. His wife tortures herself with hope while he seeks diversion elsewhere. Nell Gwynne, a woman of the theatre, little more than a common bawd, catches the kingly eye. There is no legitimate heir: the next royal babe is the actress's bastard.

In June 1668 Margaret Fell is released. Imprisoned at the king's pleasure and set free at the king's pleasure she remains praemunire, an outlaw without the protection of court or statute. Royal or judicial whim can send her back to jail.

* * * * *

Home, the bustle of welcome, smiles and tears of joy, the smell of beeswax and lavender, of good food and home brewed ale, the feel of fresh linen and polished wood. Margaret keeps Rachel's hand close in hers, and exchanges shy smiles with the small granddaughter who remained at Swarthmoor when John and Margaret Rous returned to London. She is free to love and be loved, to be at the centre of her family. She does not ask for how long. The threat of outlawry, of again being imprisoned without warning or just cause, hovers in the air. She refuses to acknowledge it openly. Her life is in the hands of God, not the king. But the worry nags at the back of her mind surfacing often enough to affect her mood and her temper.

Mary came to her, aglow with love for Thomas Lower and Margaret wanted only to damp the fire of her daughter's happiness. She would pick and prod at the character of her lover. Tom Lower smarted under 'thy mother's slights of me, and unfriendly deportment towards me'. Margaret had no real dislike of the earnest widower. Sometimes his staid pursuit of Mary, who was fourteen years younger than he, served as an uncomfortable reminder of her own Thomas. She could not explain the resultant unease. Sometimes the affair seemed merely irrelevant, something that barely touched her own life. If this marriage must take place, let it happen soon!

On 26th August 1668 Mary Fell married Thomas Lower at Swarthmoor Hall and accompanied him home to his native Cornwall. With the wedding, summer ended. Rain storms and dark skies kept Margaret within doors. She could not escape domestic concerns. Sarah thrust account books before her mother's eyes and Margaret tried to comprehend. In truth the figures panicked her. The persecution that had followed Thomas's death, her own imprisonment, marriage portions for her children, her son's extravagance, the ever increasing needs of Friends: all had cost dear. Her people suffered the oppression of the law: she would not have them suffer want as well. She must recoup money where she could. Her daughters suspected Thomas Rawlinson, Swarthmoor's ironmaster, of falsifying the forge accounts. Margaret demanded the money be repaid. For a suspected fraud of one hundred pounds, she was to hound a Friend, and once trusted servant, for two decades during which the origins of the dispute became more and more obscure. She lacked the patience to untangle rights and wrongs. Tom Rawlinson's counter accusations stung. She struck back. It was an unsavoury dispute from which no-one emerged with honour.

Margaret could not rest long at Swarthmoor, giving way to her desire for comfort, being drawn back into the small world of the Hall and its estate. God urged her to travel among Friends. While she had her freedom she would visit those in jail. Taking Rachel with her, she travelled through north-west England carrying her prayers and her hopes to Quaker prisoners. She brought news, concern for their welfare and the well being of their families. She made gifts of books, paper and pens, new stockings or a clean shirt. She heard the story of a people's faithfulness from men and women jailed for meeting together to worship God in defiance of the law. It was as if she were the hub of an enormous wheel. She must encourage, counsel, and advise that the whole might keep turning. The prisoners, at the wheel's edge, assailed by the world's evil needed her as surely as did her own family, as surely as did George Fox.

Her round of prison visits ended in Bristol. Isabel lived there now, with her husband William Yeamans. There were two grand daughters, both born during Margaret's imprisonment. She gave her heart to these babes, the tiny Margaret cocooned in her cradle and Rachel, scarce two-years-old but chattering constantly, if not always sensibly. Rachel pulled at her skirts now, gurgling for attention. She bent forward and held her tight, too tight. Infant limbs flayed outward and gurgles threatened to become screams. From somewhere the grandmother produced a trinket and the child was distracted. Sitting in her daughter's house with her grand-daughter close by, Margaret felt vulnerable in a way she had not in prison. Would this child grow up to be persecuted? God could not will it so! She banished the thought. These Quaker households were God's blessing to her. She thought of the Mary and Thomas Lower whom she would soon visit in Cornwall, and of John and Margaret Rous in London. In them lay her hope for the future: she would not fear for them.

London. December 1668. Sleet fell. The air was heavy with the smoke of chimneys. Those, with little to occupy their thoughts or their purses, cast bets on the chances of the Thames freezing. George Fox was in the capital. His business was the establishment of church government among Friends.

Margaret stayed with the Rous's. She sought out Fox almost as soon as she arrived needing to be a part of his plans, needing to be near him, to work alongside him. She knew there was dissension among Friends. There were those who would place their own leadings above those of the meeting, those who, like the dead James Nayler, would answer God's call in any way they saw fit no matter what the danger to their fellows. Now, more than ever, this people needed unity. So many had died, or languished in prison! The meetings George Fox held in London that winter were huge and powerful gatherings. Men and women, downcast and dejected, rose to their feet 'and gave open testimonies against that spirit which had seduced them from the unity of Friends'. Around them Friends opened themselves to the work of repentance and forgiveness. In prayer they brought the stray sheep back into the fold so that all were gathered in the light of God. These meetings were wondrous occasions but Fox did not want them to be needed again. The monthly and quarterly meetings he now set up would keep church discipline as well as recording sufferings and relieving poverty and want.

In the spring of 1669 Margaret travelled among Friends again, visiting meetings in Kent, Surrey and Sussex. The summer she spent in London before beginning the journey back to Bristol.

* * * * *

1669: And then it was Eleven years after my former Husbande's decease; and G. Fox being then returned from visiting Friends in Ireland. At Bristol he declared his Intentions of marriage with me...

I had seen from the Lord a considerable time before, that I should take Margaret Fell to be my

wife. And when I first mentioned it to her, she felt
the answer of Life from God thereunto.

George Fox 'declared his intentions of marriage' with her. Margaret
had no doubts. In this earthly union she saw the deepening of her
communion with God. She saw the affirmation of her leadership of
her people. She saw the transforming power of the Christ that lived
in her heart and George Fox's reaching out into the world. She saw
the love of a man for a woman.

To the world they are an ill-matched couple: the great lady and the
travelling preacher, the celibate and the widow, she ten years older
than he and the mother of eight children. Margaret does not care.
She looks at her hands. She wears no rings now, save the gold band
with which Thomas took her to wife thirty-seven years ago. He has
been dead a long time. She is tired of inhabiting a house of women
and would have a rougher edge to her sweet scented days. She places
one hand, white and delicate, in George Fox's huge, gnarled and
weathered grasp. She would taste pleasure again before it is too late.
She would love again.

Margaret is fifty-five years old. This bride keeps company with the
ageing woman in her mirror. The lack lustre locks she brushes with
care are grey-streaked. She oils skin coarsened by years and weather
and feels the thickened veins. Her eyes strain to unveil the image in
the glass. She sees the blemishes, the lines of time. She would repair
life's damage. Her hand reaches out towards the rouge pot but she
can wear no clown's mask. She will fight with other weapons: faith
and determination, a touch of arrogance, the discreet help of fine
Spanish cloth and Brussels lace. She does not appreciate the irony of
her own inconsistency.

> And the bride, the Lamb's wife, is making
> herself ready as a bride that is adorning for
> her husband. And to her is granted that she
> shall be arrayed in fine linen, clean and
> white; and the fine linen is the righteousness
> of the saints.

In search of Margaret Fell

Friends have met three times already to wait on God and consider this union. Three times have George Fox and Margaret Fell published their intention of marriage: three times has it been prayerfully accepted. It is the pattern and example that their people will follow. George Fox has also sought the agreement of Margaret's daughters and sons-in-law. He does not covet wealth, or land, or status.

Now on Wednesday, 27th October 1669, at Broadmead Meeting House in Bristol he and Margaret stand side by side in silence heavy with love and prayer.

> ...we took each other, the Lord joining us together in the honourable marriage, in the everlasting covenant and immortal Seed of life.

Margaret speaks from her heart.

> ...And likewise the saide Margaret did solemly declare that in the Everlasting power of the Mighty God and in the unalterable word and in the presence of God, his Angells and his Holy Assembly. She tooke the saide George Fox to be her Husbande...

God's will be done. Margaret Fox looks into George Fox's eyes. She feels both joy and pride. Her husband gives thanks in prayer. She hears the power, and the pain. She shares the burden of the world's evil. Hope is illusory. The marriage of the Lamb will bring no easy victory in the Lamb's War nor easy happiness to his bride.

Ten days later Margaret returned to Swarthmoor alone, while her 'Husband stayed in the Countries visiting Friends'.

* * * * *

Margaret Fox of Swarthmoor Hall was back in the great house that echoed emptily around her. It remained a house of women. Sarah, Susannah and Rachel continued to give her their love, their care and their company. She waited while the leaves fell and the days shortened. She sought the light of God in the dark days of God's year. George Fox did not come.

> I travelled through Wiltshire, Berkshire,
> Oxfordshire, and Buckinghamshire, and so
> to London; in all which counties I had many
> large and precious meetings.

The solstice came. The year turned. Aconite and snowdrop bloomed.

George Fox did not travel north.

At Marsh Grange, George Fell hankered after position and prestige in the county. Why else had he returned home, if not to mix with society? His mother heard rumours of his extravagances and his friendships. Poor insecure George! Shamed by his mother's remarriage, he needed to flaunt his acquaintance with the Kirkbys and Daniel Fleming, her enemies. He would not be damned by association. His wife, locked in her own bitterness, encouraged him. She could no more deal with her mother-in-law than she could with her grief for the two infant daughters buried in Dalton churchyard. Revenge on the woman, whose hostility, imagined or real, haunted her, seemed sweet.

'...if thou would leave Lancashire he would allow thee £200 a year, but at Swarthmore thou should not stay, and if thou would not yield to those terms, then he would get thee sent to prison', wrote John Rous of his brother-in-law, to a disbelieving Margaret.

It was folly rather than treachery. George Fell was too politically inexperienced to be anything more than a pawn in the hands of Fleming and the Kirkbys. His outlawed mother was an easy prey for the scheming magistrate.

> ...she was haled out of her house to
> Lancaster prison again.

> ...where I continued a whole Year; and most
> part of that time I was sick and weakly.

This time there was no drama, no assize court trial of the grand lady, the judge's widow. Margaret Fox was carried away to jail almost anonymously. Without an audience she did not have to be brave, or staunch in the faith, or righteous. Alone with Sarah, she shed a few honest tears of frustration and resignation. She looked on as her daughters gathered together the comforts of home, a warmer shawl, a loaf of white bread, a small flask of wine, money to pay the jailers. The April air struck cold as she rode out across the sands, a prisoner between her captors. She turned back once, looking homewards in supplication. She bowed to the will of God. There was nothing to do or say. She was a mute in a dumb show. Iron gates opened to admit her and clanged shut once more. She was aware of the grate of keys, the thud of doors closing, the rasp of rough voices as she was half led, half pushed towards a prison cell. Margaret still did not speak. She wanted nothing as much as solitude. At last they left her. She thought the tears would flow but they did not. The band around her heart tightened. She forced herself to think of the son who had brought her to this pass. She could not hate him but she mourned his weakness. Fleetingly she saw his face. There was no compassion in his look, only fear. As the image faded she glimpsed his father. Then the hurt ran deep. She almost revelled in the pain. What had they done, she and Thomas, to be blessed with such a child? She wanted to rage against the God who had allowed it to turn out so. Where was the light of God in the dungeon's dark? She thought of George Fox, her husband of six months. The prophet had not come to her.

Her body began to shake. This was no heaven-sent quaking. She put her hand to her brow and felt the cold sweat of fever. The shivering would not stop. She had to try and help herself: there was no-one else. She pulled shawl and cloak more tightly around her. What was she to her jailers but a bundle of rags, a madwoman, her speech reduced to gibberish?

As a child she had feared the witches and monsters of imagination. As a young bride she had been afraid of Thomas's physical need of her. All that was far away. Fear of childbirth or sickness was nothing to the fear she felt now. Her own shadows assaulted her. She was alone. She saw the turned backs of the men who had loved her once: her father, John Askew; Thomas; her son. George Fox's bulk loomed over her. She caught the smell of leather clothing, the scent of passion bitter-sweet, and the salt air of the Sands. The vision vanished. She was left alone in travail.

> And she brought forth a man child who was to
> rule all nations with a rod of iron: and her child
> was brought up unto God, and to his throne.
> And the woman fled into the wilderness...

She vomited. She thought she bled. She thought her body had done with that. She sweated and slept the half-sleep of fever. People came and went. She did not know who. Gentle hands tended her. They fed her broth laced with brandy. The shivering abated but her body had been torn and bruised. She seemed always to have ached. She had no wish to look in her glass. George Fox lay ill in London, his energies exhausted, his spirit brought low. He was her husband but she could not care.

Babylon lay in ruins. Margaret walked among its ashes collecting the charred fragments of the world's riches. Cloth of gold and cloth of purple. Pearls and ivory. Silk and scarlet. She touched the damp cold of her prison walls. She saw herself arrayed as a bride, anointed with perfume and decked with jewels. She wrapped her arms around her self and felt the sagging flesh of her breasts, the brittle cage of her ribs. Marriage with the Lamb had left her womb hollow. God had not filled the empty places. She wept, ugly, noisy sobs that left her face blotched and raw and her body exhausted. Comforts arrived, the bowl of scented water, soft linen handkerchiefs, possets and wine. She was scarcely aware of them.

What can we do with anguish but offer it to God? Yet God cannot take what we refuse to give. I sit with a woman whose son died thirty years ago. She tends a shrine. Deep red dahlias stand in a cut glass vase beneath his portrait. A young man in uniform grins eternally at the camera. She is a good woman, a hard-working woman. Each good deed, each flower arranged before a church altar is her boy's memorial but she holds tight to the bitterness of loss. God cannot staunch her bleeding.

* * * * *

Margaret Fox's second imprisonment lasted twelve months, from April 1670 to April 1671. In May 1670, Parliament passed the Second Conventicle Act, confirming dissent as a crime against the state and condoning intolerance and injustice yet again. In London, during the summer, militia men seized meeting houses. In August William Penn and William Meade were arrested and sent to trial for speaking at a Meeting held in the street. Their acquittal by a jury in the face of the judge's hostility made legal history as a victory for civil liberties. Immediately it changed nothing. Persecution continued.

On 14th October 1670 George Fell died, aged thirty-two. His wife Hannah, a baby son and a two-year-old daughter survived him. Hannah Fell never learned to love her Quaker relatives, and they struggled to forgive her hostility.

Margaret was discharged under the Broad Seal, the sentence of praemunire ended. The king and his council were merciful men.

A free woman walked in an April garden. Spring sunshine warmed her. Somewhere a blackbird called.

In August 1671 George Fox followed his leading to carry truth to America. Margaret could only wish him God speed. George was taken ill in Barbados: much later there was a letter. From Jamaica she heard that 'Friends are generally well; and there is a convincement: but things would be too large to write of'. And then silence for weeks or months at a time. He was away for two years: his wife could not share the excitement or the danger. It was not her enterprise.

* * * * *

> Concerning the women's meetings; encourage
> all the women of families that are convinced,
> and mind virtue and love truth, and walk in it,
> that they may come up into God's service, that
> they may be serviceable in their generation and
> in the creation…so that none may stand idle
> out of the vineyard, and out of the service…

'She saw him first at Kendal fair…'

'Her mother was never sure about the match.'

'The child was in no hurry to be born. A time we had of it, with her screaming as if the devil was at her back…'

'They took him from the meeting house to the jail.'

'The little one is too quiet, too pale faced.'

'Has she not weaned that babe yet?'

'She can't get herself and the infant to Lancaster.'

'There's too much weeping and too little prayer in that quarter. And when did she last sweep that house?'

'But thou shalt go sister, and take the clothes that Elizabeth's youngest outgrew this month past. What a great lump of a child that is!'

'Take a loaf.'

'Shalt thou spare a jug of milk from thine own cow?'

'Tom Carter must take her to Lancaster. She will be the better for seeing the husband, if they let her…'

'Can we find lodgings for her with Friends in the city?'

'Aye, but we must find money too, for her travel and her food.'

'Take her our love, sister.'

'And pray with her. Hold her safe in the light of God. Hold them all safe.'

* * * * *

> ...and in your day's work, do it not negligently,
> not with careless minds, but be you diligent in
> every one of your women's meetings...

The white walls and plain wooden benches of a country meeting house. Bent heads, bonnets. Hair severely tamed: stray curls display the vanity of youth. The skirts are the work-a-day colours of home-spun wool, the greys and browns of country tweeds. An apron gleams white. A flash of coloured stocking is quickly hidden. One woman struggles to sit comfortably with the weight of her pregnancy: another fights off the stiffness of age. A cough, a sigh. A bench creaks. Stillness, silence. Faces are at rest. The soft bloom of young womanhood and the rough cheeks of farmwives used to being out in all weathers. The turmoil within is masked, hidden, admitted, given to God. They have God's work to do.

> Mary Gore's daughter the last meeting was to go to live with James Laithwaite, She refused to live there; Friends having had the thing under consideration, Friends do order the said girl to return to her place again, if she refuse to take Friends advice in the matter, her mother is not to entertain her, but to turn her out and let her fend for herself.

> It is advised by this meeting that Friends do not let their daughters or servants go to the 'paistry' schools with the world's children but teach them at home what is decent and of good report in that matter.

> It is thought fit that six women Friends be appointed to hear what Enoch Tomlinson hath to say for himself concerning his clearness from his former proceeding with Sarah Tarbuck....

* * * * *

At Swarthmoor Hall, Sarah Fell, first clerk to Swarthmoor Women's Monthly Meeting, labours long hours, making a meticulous record of her meeting's care and concern.

> ...pd of the weomens Meetinge stocke to ffriends of Hawxheade Meettinge that they gave to a woman for lookeinge to Tomasin Sawrey when she was sicke
>
> ...000 03 00.

> ...pd of the weomens stocke...to Ann Birkett who is poore & in Necessity ...
>
> 000 05 00.

* * * * *

> That the young ones when they feel the Lord to open their hearts in a few words by way of Testimony, that they be very carefull, not to utter more words than the Lord requires... when a few words – fitly spoken, from the savour of life, would be as apples of Gold in pictures of silver and would be more refreshing, and answer the life in another as face answers face in a glass.

The young will ever be chided by those whose grey hair gives them wisdom. The minute comes from the London Box Meeting. Its authors chose their words carefully. In truth, they wanted an end to rambling spoken ministry from bold young women intent on remaining on their feet until they had seen just which young men were in meeting. The rebuke is tenderly put. 'Answer the life in another as face answers face in a glass': it was how they tried to pass on tradition.

* * * * *

It was a quiet revolution. It did no more than recognise work women had always done. Yet it confirmed their right to meddle in the things of God.

There were still those that denied that right. When have there ever not been?

John Wilkinson and John Story would have no meddling. Margaret faced them alone. George Fox did not return from America until 1673 and was almost immediately imprisoned in Worcester. His wife tried to hold her opponents in the love of God, but John Story she had never liked and his aggression served only to provoke her own. What could she do to stop the drift into schism by those intent on achieving it? The issues had become too many and too complex. Would that this dispute was merely about women's meetings! There was talk enough about propriety and what it was right and proper for women to do or not do. But this was not the nub of the matter. George Fox's leadership was being called into question. The ripples of criticism threatened his wife's standing. John Wilkinson and his faction found too much to anger them in the very establishment of church government. For them the voice of the living God demanded an immediate response, not the measured deliberations of a meeting, whether it be of men or women. Margaret knew they were wrong.

She sat in Swarthmoor Monthly Women's Meeting and listened to the women voicing their concerns. She watched the quiet authority with which her daughter Sarah clerked this meeting. She loved Sarah's eager attention, her ready memory for names and faces. A woman stood, hesitant, reluctant to begin. The meeting held her in its love, in God's light. They heard her into speech.

> And now Dear Friend we are truly comforted
> in our Meetings and Gatherings...
>
> We being met together in fear of the Lord, to
> wait upon him for his ancient power, to order
> us, and, in his wisdom and counsel to guide us
> in our exercise relating to church affairs: it
> hath pleased him to break in among us in a
> glorious manner, to our great satisfaction, and
> he hath filled our meeting with his living pres-
> ence, and crowned our assembly with his

> heavenly power, and opened the fountain of
> life unto us, and caused the streams of his love
> freely to flow among us, and run from vessel to
> vessel, to the gladding of our hearts...

It did not matter that they were subject to the men's meetings, at least not yet.

I stand in a kitchen, crowded with women, setting potatoes to bake in a recalcitrant oven. Soup simmers, steam rises, the teacups multiply, pots are washed and dried.

'She minds those grandchildren far too often.'

'It was cancer.'

'The woman's refuge. She had nowhere else...'

'She's their financial adviser.'

'They think it's Alzheimer's...'

'There's no money. She only ever worked part-time because of the children.'

'She does too much.'

'She went to Australia.'

'She just went...'

Someone sings, 'Woman am I,
        Spirit am I.
        I am the infinite within myself...
        I can find no beginning
        I can see no end
        All this I am.'

It is time to give attention to our business.

> And therefore dear Friends and Sisters, all
> up, and be doing, and put your hands to the
> work and your shoulders to the burden...

* * * * *

The political wheel of fortune turned once more. Charles II, the man of little faith, continued to play games with other men's creeds. The shadow of the Sun King, Louis XIV, hung over the English court. By the Treaty of Dover, he agreed to pay Charles both to fight the Dutch and to declare himself a Catholic. The war was prepared for openly. The promise of conversion remained secret. Englishmen had no love of France or the Pope. In March 1672, on the eve of his second Dutch War, Charles issued the Declaration of Indulgence, which suspended the penal laws against dissenters and papists. The Great Pardon freed five hundred Quaker prisoners, the royal prerogative of mercy. Parliament, suspecting a bid to extend the king's power, launched a counter attack. The Test Act of 1673 debarred Roman Catholics and Protestant nonconformists alike from public office and forced James, Duke of York, heir to the throne, to resign as Lord High Admiral. Catholicism ousted dissent from the forefront of English politics without giving dissenters any guarantee of safety.

> Dear Heart, Thou seemedst to be a little
> grieved when I was speaking of prisons, and
> when I was taken; be content with the will of
> the Lord God…

December 1673: Fox was arrested and imprisoned in Worcester jail. The charge was a fabrication. The justices expected to catch him in meeting but they tarried too long on the way and the Quaker was arrested while talking with Friends in the parlour, hardly a crime, even in Charles II's England.

Margaret could not be content. She did not want him broken by prison. In Worcester he 'fell sick, in a long, lingering sickness, and many times was very ill'. She loved him in the Light of God but she also loved him as a wife.

She was not the only woman left at Swarthmoor struggling with the loneliness of separation. Thomas Lower followed Fox to jail to serve as his secretary. His wife, Mary, nursed her newborn daughter and her own fears. The days were full but the waiting was no easier for that. Margaret grew weary of the unending need to petition authority, of the need to follow legal paths as ill defined and subject to change as the tracks across the sands.

George Fox was sent from Worcester to London to appear before the King's Bench. She sent him a salmon from the river Duddon: poached fish for an invalid diet. There was something incongruous in delicacies sent to jail. She wanted to ease his imprisonment: she sent money to pay the jailers. He used it to pay for a length of black cloth sent to her by carrier. She was both hurt and touched. The lawyers conveyed Fox back to Worcester and again to London. At times he was free in all but name. What he was denied was release with honour. His sickness became worse. Friends who nursed him feared for his life.

Margaret went to Worcester. She did not want to. She was afraid. Did God want her husband to die a martyr's death in a prison cell? Once there she could only wait through seventeen long weeks. She watched George's face so closely that she dreamt his features and their changes. Each rasping breath, each visible heartbeat was hers as well. In attention she found prayer: in prayer she found attention. She knew the full dimension of her love.

> After this, the said George Fox's Wife went up
> to London, and made Application to the
> King, who spake kindly to her, and referred
> her to the Lord-Keeper, who told her, that
> the King could not release her Husband any
> otherwise than by a Pardon.

Fox could do nothing but refuse. Acceptance would have meant admission of a crime of which he was innocent. It was an understanding Margaret shared: the heartache continued.

In February 1675 Fox appeared again before the King's Bench. The court proved the errors of the original indictment and he was released. Undiminished in spirit and stronger in body, he took his place at the centre of the Yearly Meeting in May. Margaret, tired of London, wanted her own hearth, her own people and her husband.

> ...and I was very desirous to go home with
> him, which we did.

God made her a gift of nearly two years in which they lived together as man and wife. As her love deepened so did her faith: she knew that the two were but parts of a single whole.

Despite his broken health George Fox's sense of urgency is undiminished. Confined within doors, surrounded by the letters and papers that carry the memories of his life's work, he can still talk in a voice from which the fire of youth has not departed. Margaret listens as intently as she ever did, although now she listens to more than words. She hears him fight for breath. She fears the gauntness of his frame, the clumsiness of his movements. She can only guess at the effort each one costs. She watches him struggle to mop his brow with a handkerchief and return his attention to the letter before him. Her heart reaches out to the sick man. Somehow, she has never imagined that he might be the first to die. She fights to hold him in God's keeping and suppress her own desires.

Stoicism in the face of sickness was a necessity: there were few palliatives and fewer cures. Fox was a man driven by his own sense of God's purpose, firm in spirit and physically strong. His broken body began to heal. Other, frailer, souls were given up to God. While Margaret nursed her husband, two of her daughters watched their daughters die. The infant Margaret Lower was four months short of her second birthday. Rachel Yeamans was ten. Such little lives. They buried Rachel at Sunbrick and gave alms to the poor.

The interlude came to an end. At the end of March 1677 Fox left Swarthmoor for Sedbergh and Westmoreland. His God both drove him and protected him. Winter clung fast to the countryside.

'Dear Heart', he wrote to Margaret,

> ...The road was many times deep and bad
> with snow, our horses sometimes were down,
> and we were not able to ride; and sometimes
> we had great storms and rain; but by the
> power of the Lord I went through all.

> ...he was but weakly, and unable to ride well,
> but the Lord supported him.

And thence south to London, to Harwich where he took ship for Holland, from there to Germany. The love of God and of the woman who was his wife went with him.

Margaret has passed her sixtieth birthday. The woman in her mirror is grey-haired, the lines more deeply etched on her face. She looks out at the bay beyond her window. A narrow strip of sand shows yellow-brown. A gull screeches. The thin autumn sunlight flecks the grey expanse of sea. Like the tide, her energy ebbs and flows. She refuses to give way to loneliness, resting in the love of God and the love of her people. God grants her the deepening of faith that is the result of faithfulness.

Somewhere I read: 'Heaven is nothing else but willing and working in quiet love' – love that is undramatic, that nourishes and sustains in adversity, that reflects the love of God. Is this the ultimate gift of faith, the ability to love here on this imperfect earth?

Margaret Fox, Quaker, has grown older, perhaps wiser, but the fire of youth has not been quenched by time. The passionate woman compelled to proclaim her truth to a disbelieving world, lives on behind the mask of age. 'What canst thou say?' The memory is as strong now as it had ever been. She can see George Fox in Ulverston church, hear the roar of the prophet's voice.

> ...what canst thou say? Art thou a child of
> Light and hast walked in the Light, and what
> thou speakest is it inwardly from God?

Oh! She has 'walked in the Light' but she has walked in the realms of darkness too. She knows so much, has experienced so much; but she knows nothing! Like the blind beggar led by the hand, she must trust the God who lights her womanly heart! She must go forward in faith, owning both the wonderful simplicity and the awesome complexity of God's presence within and without her. She will not admit impossibility. God is and God can... The choices, the chances, the possibilities are infinite now as they were in the beginning. The suffering, the beatings, the constant imprisonments, the fines and poverty, the innumerable consequences, great and small, of persecution have to be accepted as part of God's plan. And the deaths? She sees Will Caton's boyish face haloed in light. She wishes...but it is not hers to wish. He is with God. She must look to the future. She writes to the young William Penn,

> Dear and faithful; whom ye Lord hath chosen, and owned and honoured with his everlasting Truth, who hath manifested thyself to be a true follower of the Lamb, Blessed art thou for ever, that hath chosen that good part...

The Daughter of Sion Awakened (1677) was to be her last long tract. Her urgency is as great, the pace of her writing as fast, as in those first heady days. The images of light and dark, the Biblical references, tumble after one another on to the page. She writes in haste and she writes surely.

> Out of Sion, the Perfection of Beauty, hath God shined, in the Light of his glorious Son...to redeem his whole Body, which is his church...

> Now the universal, divine, glorious, infinite, invisible God is shining in the dark places, in the hearts of men and women.

Margaret is awed by her own certainty, the certainty that Christ is come again in the heart. His power grips her: she trembles before it.

> But Christ Jesus shakes all Foundations that are not built upon him; and he is coming to rase out and to root out that Foundation on

which the old serpent hath laid in the Hearts of People...he was before ever the old serpent was, he was set up from everlasting to everlasting; man and woman was created in his Image, and he is now coming to claim his own, and to recover and restore man again.

She sees the Garden of Eden, blazing heat after summer rain, pure white flowers against rich green foliage. The serpent, at once hypnotic and repellent, beguiles Eve. Eve, no longer innocent, tempts Adam. They eat the forbidden fruit. An angry God denounces their disobedience. They are exiled from Paradise, from God's grace. Darkness covers the earth. Now, God promises Paradise regained.

He is now coming to claim his own, and to recover and restore man again.

The darkness of the apostasy, of the false church, will give way to the light of God's presence.

So here lies all the world of the Ungodly, guilty of Sin, guilty of Transgression, guilty of Disobedience; but now in these last dayes, the Lord Jesus Christ is come a Light into the World, that whosoever believeth in him, should not perish, but have everlasting Life, and that through him they might be saved.

So this Light, that lights every man that comes into the world, this is the true Light, that shines in the dark heart, and this is the true Day, that dawns in the heart; and Christ Jesus is the Day-Star that ariseth in the heart.

The day star of her heart: she rejoices in God's presence there. God's time was coming.

The new heaven will be here on earth. Christ is building his temple 'which is made of living stones…he is building up spiritual Sion, the city of his Solemnity, the wise Master-builder is at work…'

In the light of Christ lies the hope of perfection, freely given to all God's people.

> …he is able to save to the utmost all that ever comes unto God by him, which believeth in his Light, and walketh in it, of what Nation or People soever, Jew or Gentile, Barbarian, Scythian, Bond or Free, Male or Female…

She pictures the Kingdom, the Holy City, the river of the water of life and the throne of God. 'Blessed are they that do his Command-ments, that they may have the right to the Tree of Life, and enter in through the Gates into the City.'

She stands in the light of God, sure of its power to change every man and woman here on earth, to transform her world.

* * * * *

With her words as my guide I journey towards understanding. I too want to walk in the company of God's people guided by the light of God's love. I want to claim Jesus of Nazareth, teacher, healer, prophet, as the day-star of my heart. I go on pilgrimage.

In the magic of islands, in a landscape coloured by heather and bracken I find God. In the remoteness of the place and its stark beauty God is.

In a stone cottage at the sea's edge, in a room lit by candles and warmed by a peat fire, we linger over the remains of a meal. We cling fast to the magic, the escape from reality, loath to abandon the intimacy that comes from the knowledge that tomorrow we must all move on or go back. Conversation falters. Volleys of words give way to silence, and into the silence flow the words of the Eucharist. We meet again in prayer, savouring companionship in the doughy newness of the communion bread, the loaf that Gabriella baked that afternoon. We offer one another 'the body of Christ' and the accents of North America mingle with those of Glasgow and Edinburgh. The twang of Tasmania answers a voice more used to speaking in German. Southern England blends into Europe.

In that moment it does not matter who and what we are. The labels we wear, Presbyterian, Catholic, Anglican, Lutheran, Quaker, vanish. In communion with my neighbours and with God I realise what it could be to build one church. I am brought face to face with the possibility that faith can transform my world. And recognition of that possibility is of itself a homecoming.

* * * * *

A woman walks alone in a garden from which the colours of summer are fading. In solitude she finds the beauty of God's world. The sombre black green of yew. The last roses, the first fallen leaves. Voices, too distant to be distinct. Horses on the lane. The snort of cattle in the meadow. The shrill prattle of children. The shadow of the house. The scent of home. The moment is but a moment. In it she sees the grace of God.

Margaret Fox waited for her husband's return. He came back in the September of 1678, riding across the Sands as summer started to mellow into autumn. He had travelled north slowly, gathering his people anew.

> …I went to Swarthmore; and it being the meeting-day there, I had a sweet opportunity with Friends, our hearts being opened in the love of God, and his blessed life flowing amongst us.

He stayed above a year but he could not remain in the isolation of Furness. He was not to return. Margaret was accepting. In May 1681, she rode south herself, accompanying her daughter Sarah who was to marry William Meade. The journey had become overly familiar, no longer new and exciting but fraught with vexation. Dust and drizzle alike irritated her throat. She was afflicted with a persistent cough and longed to breathe the pure air of home. London plagued her with its crowds and its noise. She did her duty by the yearly meeting of Friends gathered in the capital, saw Sarah safely wed and turned northward once more. Rachel was at Swarthmoor to welcome her mother home and look to her needs. Did Margaret fear losing her youngest daughter's loving care when she opposed her marriage to Daniel Abraham, or did she object to a young man of twenty two courting her thirty year old daughter? Whatever its cause, Margaret's ill will passed over as quickly and as violently as a summer storm. Young Daniel shared his late father's easy humour and Margaret had both liked and respected John Abraham. Mother and daughter embraced and were reconciled. Rachel was married at home and Daniel accepted the need to live at Swarthmoor. His mother-in-law would always be cared for.

Margaret is within sight of her seventieth birthday. She has almost accomplished her allotted span of three score years and ten. She does not fear death but she fights old age. Her daughters are alternately surprised by the strength of her faith and the force of her opinions and alarmed by her seeming failure to grasp the details of the everyday. Sometimes she is amused by their reactions and sometimes she minds. Sarah, ever managing, wrote from London explaining a debt Margaret owed Susannah.

> ...and this is as full and plaine an acct as I can give, which I hope will be thy understanding and satisfaction; thus much I writt you formerly, which you were satisfied withal that time; but then it goes out of your mindes againe; and it seems strange to you afterwards having not thought of it a pretty time.

Her mother accepted the rebuke and inevitably let it slip to the back of her mind. Susannah fretted for her money and Sarah counselled her sister Rachel Abraham 'to put it downe in a booke by way of Acct'.

Mothers and daughters: the relationships change. I give way to the temptation to make my mother's decisions about trains or Christmas or warm clothes. It's the need to do things at speed, embarrassment at the hesitancy of age, the habit of management or motherhood. It's the recognition of a life-long bond.

Margaret missed the bustle and impatience to get things done that was Sarah. It was in this daughter that she most easily recognised her own younger self. She did not have that energy now. Sarah had cared for her mother, for Swarthmoor and its people for a long time. She was thirty-nine when she married William Meade. Margaret was not sure if she wished her a child before it was too late or the safety of an empty womb. She rejoiced in the birth of Sarah's son in May 1684. Her daughter wrote,

> I was about six hours in travail, and though it
> was sharp the Lord was good to me in giving
> me strength to go through it and endure it
> and gave me deliverance in his own good
> time of a sweet babe.

Margaret in her turn sent 'kind motherly advice about suckling the infant'. She knew the risk of death in the first months of life: she willed this child to be healthy and thriving. She wanted Sarah's happiness. She wished her joy in motherhood and also the companionship that she sometimes felt was missing from her own life. Once long ago she and Thomas had shared the joys and sorrows of their children's growing up, and exchanged news of the small world that was home. Yet there had always been gaps they could not fill. She had never known Thomas's Lancaster or London, the law or Parliament, nor had she fully understood the way he must always question and analyse things that were of the spirit. And her marriage to George Fox? Would she want that for her daughters?

* * * * *

1683 and 1684: the winters were bitter. The Thames froze. London Friends were locked out of their meeting houses. They met in snow-covered streets. Authority would have no more dissent.

The king would have authority. Against a background of plot and counter-plot, spies and informers, Charles edged towards absolute monarchy. The last Parliament of the reign met in royalist Oxford in 1681. The Commons was intent on the exclusion of the Catholic James, Duke of York, from the succession to the throne. Parliament was dismissed within a week: the king would have none of it. Charles wanted security. The Popish Plot seemed to threaten Protestantism. The Exclusion Crisis and the move to make the Duke of Monmouth, his illegitimate son by Lucy Walters, heir to the throne threatened his brother's right of succession. The Rye House Plot threatened his life. Charles was forced into alliance with the Anglican Church. He would no longer rouse the nation's suspicions by dallying with dissent. The last years of his reign were years of intense persecution. Yet, with Charles there would always be a final act of inconsistency. He would not tolerate nonconformity but in February 1681 he granted William Penn, Quaker, license to settle Pennsylvania. England's colonial interest transcended religious difference. At home the people of God called Quakers were harried by the magistrates.

> 1683: Margaret Fox, for suffering Meetings at her House in Swarthmore, was fined by the Name of Margaret Fell, and had taken from her, at one Time, Cattle worth 30£ 0s 0d
> And at another Time,
>
> to the value of   <u>40£ 0s 0d</u>
>
>   70£ 0s 0d
>
> When Thomas Lower, on her Behalf, demanded a Copy of the warrant in order to demand an Appeal, the Officers said, They durst not give it, the Justices having charged them to the contrary. So they sold her Cattle, and rendred no Account thereof.

They took her to Lancaster jail again, together with Rachel and Daniel Abraham. She was held prisoner for less than three weeks but she was weary of the call to witness thus. She kept her meeting at her house. She would not pay tithes. She would not swear oaths. She had been arraigned and fined as a widow despite the fourteen years that had passed since her second marriage. It made money for the justices: for her, it opened half-forgotten wounds, the talk, overheard long ago, of the nature of her relationship with George Fox. She had been convicted on the false evidence of a sheep stealer and a man who had lived for seven years on the profits of a woman's theft. The corruption angered her. The persecution drove her to protest at court, as she had always protested.

> So I was moved to go to London in the 70th
> year of my age, and the Word was in me.

To Charles II Margaret wrote,

> Be pleased to Remember, that at Thy first
> Coming to Reign in this Kingdom, I was here
> to Inform Thee concerning the State and
> Condition of the Lord's people called Quaker;
> And at that time the King was pleased to
> promise Liberty to Tender Consciences, so
> long as they lived peaceably under his
> Government. And I then desired no more of
> the King, than he would forbear persecuting of
> them, until he had just cause for their
> Disloyalty.

Margaret petitioned a dying king who found no amusement in the pleas of an old woman and who looked to his own conscience, not that of Fox's people. At the last he summoned a Catholic priest and made his peace with the faith of his mother and his brother.

James, Duke of York, became King James II. The nation let him succeed. The ill-fated attempt to put the Duke of Monmouth, Charles' illegitimate son, on the throne scarcely spread beyond the

West Country for all that it ended with the horrific warning of Judge Jeffreys' Bloody Assize. England had a Catholic king with a Catholic wife but the country wanted no long-term link with Rome. Religion and politics still walked hand in hand: the relationship had changed. James wanted freedom of worship for Roman Catholics. His bargaining counter was the toleration of dissent. What he did not foresee was the possibility of an alliance between nonconformists and Anglicans. In 1687 the king issued a Declaration of Indulgence suspending the laws against dissent. When he re-issued the same declaration in the following year the Anglican clergy refused to read it from their pulpits,

> Not from any want of tenderness to Dissen-
> ters...but because that Declaration is founded
> upon such a dispensing power as hath often
> been declared illegal in parliament.

The established church took a stand, not against toleration, but against absolutism. Yet it was less James' religious policy than the prospect of its continuance that drove men towards revolution. On 10th June 1688 Mary of Modena, now queen of England, gave birth to a son. Within six months she had carried him to exile in France. Her husband followed her. Anne Hyde's daughter Mary sat on the English throne alongside her Dutch Protestant husband, William III. The shades of Cromwell's revolution were, at least partially, laid to rest. The Toleration Act granted limited freedom of worship and suspended the penal laws against nonconformity, but the English establishment would remain firmly Anglican for more than a century. Roman Catholics were debarred from Parliament. Public office and university education remained the preserve of those who could take Anglican Communion.

It was a more tolerant world, just.

In Ulverston Market they traded on for coppers and small silver. Cattle lowed: the air carried the stench of dung. The daughter of a remote farm sold butter and cheese with the sweetness of her smile, and pictured the powder, paint and patches she would never possess. A clutch of coloured ribbons, bought for a penny, would feed her daydreams and earn her mother's disapproval. An old woman walked by, bent low over her stick. A passing schoolboy mimicked her steps and was cuffed for his impudence. Outside the inn two drunkards lolled, decrying the manners if not the morals of their world. St Mary's Church still stood in the shelter of its hill. No bells rang. The priest was an Anglican parson. Squire, small trader and farmhand alike snoozed gently through Sunday sermons. The parson collected his tithe.

Lancashire 1690:

> The tithe of Corn taken in kind this Year
> from the People called Quakers in this
> County amounted to 134£ 14s 5d.

The world changed but slowly. Slowly, God's 'peculiar people' found a new way of living with the world.

> Walk wisely and circumspectly towards all
> men, in the peaceable spirit of Christ Jesus,
> giving no offence nor occasions to those in
> outward government, nor way to any contro-
> versies, heats or distractions of this world,
> about the kingdom's thereof.

So read the Yearly Meeting epistle for 1689. Fox's great people had been gathered. The nature of their calling had altered.

> The Quaker, too, had ceased to prophesy in
> public against steeple houses, and had
> become a thrifty dealer, studying to be quiet.

There's a grain of truth there, but a grain of kindness? Yet, what a people who had been persecuted for two generations most wanted was quiet and rest and recovery. Margaret Fox wrote to William III,

And now God has placed thee over us, in this Government, who hast been very moderate and merciful to us, and we live very comfortably under thee and it, and do enjoy our Meetings quietly...

* * * * *

George Fox died on 13th January 1691. Margaret was at Swarthmoor. She hadn't wanted to be with him at the end. She didn't know why. Perhaps in his passing she saw her own. Perhaps she wanted to cling to her memories. She had gone to London to see him six months before, making the slow journey south by coach, answering the will of God. She found her husband 'better in his health and strength than many times I had seen him before'. She left him in the care of his people until God chose to gather him to Himself.

She was thankful for the Friends who had tended him at the end. She understood the fullness of the love that was given to both of them. All she could do was return it.

> ...my Heart was rejoyced, to feel the Ancient Love and Unity of the Eternal Spirit amongst you.

What is love if it is not a rejoicing heart? Now, she could look back on the years of their marriage with understanding. The heartache of separation was suffered in God's service. Fox could no more have taken root in the 'outward habitation' that was Swarthmoor, than she could have abandoned it for him.

> ...so that we were very willing both of us, to live apart for some years on God's account, and his truth's service, and to deny ourselves of that comfort which we might have had in being together, for the sake and service of the Lord and his truth.

...And now he hath finished his course, and his testimony, and is entered into his eternal rest and felicity. I trust in the same powerful God, that his holy arm and power will carry me through, whatever he hath yet for me to do; and he will be my strength and support, and the bearer up of my head unto the end, and in the end.

Margaret Fox, widow. She is alone. She sits before the great fireplace, willing the flames to warm her. Her body gives way to the desolation of bereavement. She is an old woman with an old woman's brittle frame and sagging flesh. She cannot fight off this winter chill. She pulls her shawl more closely around her shoulders. She does not weep. That, at least, is the fruit of suffering. She looks down at her hands. The thumbs are twisted: they do not move easily. The judge's wedding band still circles her finger. It is the prophet she thinks of. From somewhere long ago, the echo of excitement and danger reaches her. She is an old woman: she dozes.

The light of God. It no longer rips her open as it once did. The light is her comforter. Her Christ speaks to her,

> And ye now therefore have sorrow: but I will
> see you again, and your heart shall rejoice,
> and your joy no man taketh from you.

She has no fear: she tries to understand. 'Whatever He hath yet for me to do'. Her life has not yet run its course.

She sits on in her own stillness. She listens. Her daughter's voice. A child's crying hushed. Metal-toed boots on stone flags. Laughter. The scrape of a chair on a wooden floor. A dog barks. Serving maids rattle dishes. More wood is thrown on the fire.

She is not alone. God is with her. God leads her and guides her yet. She hears Rachel's light tread in the room. A small boy stomps beside her. The younger woman helps the older to rise. Margaret draws herself upright: no matter that hers is the bent figure of age. She

In search of Margaret Fell

moves towards the table: she feels, rather than sees, her grandson's smile answer hers. Wooden bowls, broth and bread: childhood and old age.

First day Meeting. Friends no longer meet at the Hall. Shortly before his death, George Fox gave them the meeting house on Swarthmoor Lane. They take her in the carriage. She cannot walk or ride even that short length of road, not in winter. Perhaps when spring comes. The horses stop, the door opens. Daniel Abraham takes her arm. She struggles to remember the names of young men and women who remind her of Friends she once knew. She finds her place on a bench. Looking up, she stills the shuffling beside her. She is aware of other arrivals, of a door closing. She loses herself in the silence and in the care of her people. God wills her to go on.

> For I know his faithfulness and goodness,
> and I have experience of his love; to whom
> be glory and powerful dominion for ever.

She knows the love of God and the love of her people. She loves them too well to have them sink into disunity in these more tolerant times. She struggles to make herself heard, chiding Friends, as once she chided her children, too often sounding merely querulous. Friends should accept the right to affirm instead of taking an oath and not quarrel with the form of words they are required to use. She cannot stop them arguing over the words. For more than two decades there are those who will affirm 'in the presence of God' and those who will not. In the end the government gives way and asks only that they 'solemnly declare and affirm' in the presence of the law. Plain dress, the dull uniformity of Quaker grey, saddens a woman whose memory holds the joy of a rainbow and the coloured silks of her youth. Moreover what is fashion, however plain, but an outward form, a 'silly, poor gospel' to the Christ who lives in the heart? But it was the gospel the next generation would have. The old woman can criticise but not convince. The future is not hers.

In the stillness of the early afternoon the old women walk the landscape of the past. The street violence of the General Strike. Children had to be collected from school: my grandmother forgot. Long after dark her daughters were rescued from the care of a terrified teacher. In Buff Place the mob overturned a bus. A seven-year-old looked on, afraid. There were no holidays. The lucky ones went hop-picking. The hops were always 'as big as your thumb'.

Fragments of memory: they are my inheritance, part of what I am. In owning them I claim the freedom to travel on.

In those last years Margaret does not often leave Furness. There is one final journey to London.

There are letters.

> Dear Friends, Brethren and Sisters
>
> ...And now it is good for us all to go on and continue hand in hand in the unity and fellowship of this eternal Spirit, in humility and lowlyness of mind, each affirming others better than ourselves.

There is always fellowship and the strength that comes from God.

> But they that wait upon the Lord shall renew their strength; they shall mount up with wings as eagles; they shall run, and not be weary; and they shall walk and not faint.

Margaret Fox waited upon God and with God. Her spirit was strong and her heart full. She knew Christ's way was the only way. She wrote to her grandchildren 'desiring you to keep close to the Lord, your love and life...'. She knew what it was to make the pilgrimage and to fail. In the light of God she had the courage to name her failures to herself. Her sister. Her son. Poor tortured James Nayler. Thomas Rawlinson? Her own Thomas? She did not know. The past was in God's keeping.

She needed the warmth of a fire whatever the season. She kept her shawl close around her shoulders. She dozed and dreamt and woke again. In the deep tones of Thomas Lower and Daniel Abraham she heard John Camm and Richard Farnsworth, Francis Howgill and her beloved Will Caton. In the childish treble of her grandson she heard her own son. She saw her daughters as the infants clinging to her skirts and as the women they became. For a moment she caught the melancholy look in her mother's eyes as they rested on the grave face of John Askew. She felt Rachel's warm hand in her cold one. There was no need for words. She looked into the face of George Fox as he stood in Ulverston church on a far distant day.

She has learned to strip away outward things. She knows the impermanence of our hold on earth. The simplicity that is in Christ is almost hers. She would make her peace with God and wait in His stillness.

She would 'fasten her minde upon the Lord, which will bee her only repose, and comfort and never matter nor minde outward things but lett them hang of themselves...'

> And the Blessed God of Heaven and Earth
> preserved her in a good Understanding to
> the last: And in the time of her sickness she
> was in a sweet Frame of Spirit.

God beckoned her. She knew the separation of body and spirit, the freedom that is the final, undeniable knowledge of God's presence. All joy was there, and all sorrow too.

> She died at Swarthmore Hall in Furneis in
> Lancashire, the 23rd Day of the Second
> Month, 1702 being near the 88th Year of her
> Age; and was Bury'd in the Burying Ground
> at Sunbrecke, belonging to Swarthmore
> Meeting-House, the 27th of the Same
> Month...

April. A clump of primroses bloom at the roadside. The sheep baa, protecting their lambs. A farm cart brings the coffin up the lane from the sea. Her daughters, their husbands, her grandchildren, Friends walk behind it, dry-eyed.

> ...we believe she is inheriting a Heavenly Mansion, prepared by the Lord Jesus Christ, for all his faithful Followers.

A hazy sun shines in an overcast sky, blue grey like the sands and the sea. The branches of straggling ash trees tremble in the breeze.

> And I saw a new heaven and a new earth...

On the strand below Marsh Grange a young woman stands alone. The tide is on the ebb, the sand unmarked. Impatiently she discards her shoes, gathers her skirts in her arms and runs towards the distant hills,

...towards the glory of the morning, and the glory of the Kingdom.

> The Truth is one and the same always, and though ages and generations pass away, and one generation goes and another comes, yet the word and power and spirit of the Living God endures for ever, and is the same and never changes.

* * * * *

Select Bibliography

The most detailed biographical studies of Margaret Fell are:

Margaret Fell, Mother of Quakerism by Isabel Ross first published in 1949 and most recently reprinted by Sessions in 1996.

Margaret Fell and the Rise of Quakerism by Bonnelyn Kunze (Macmillan 1994).

Women and Quakerism in the Seventeenth Century by Christine Trevett (Sessions 1995) is a useful, and very readable, study of the lives and roles of first and second generation Quaker women.

A selection of Margaret Fell's writings which includes her brief auto-biography, an account of her trial at Lancaster in 1664, and some tracts and letters was published in 1710 under the cumbersome title,

A Brief Collection of Remarkable Passages and Occurrences Relating to the Birth, Education, Life, Conversion, Travels, Services, and Deep Sufferings of that Ancient, Eminent, and Faithful Servant of the Lord Margaret Fell; but by her second marriage, Margaret Fox.

Margaret Fell's account of her life and some of the letters from *A Brief Collection* are included in *Hidden in Plain Sight. Quaker Women's Writings 1650-1700* edited by Mary Garman, Judith Applegate, Margaret Benefiel and Dortha Meredith (Pendle Hill 1996).

The bulk of the primary source material for Margaret Fell's life is to be found in the manuscript collection in the library of Friends House. The Swarthmore Manuscripts consist of eight volumes of material, for the most part letters, many of which are addressed to Margaret Fell or George Fox. Volume III of the Spence Manuscripts contains about two hundred letters and epistles written by Margaret Fell. The Abraham Manuscripts are a smaller collection of letters and other items that passed into possession of the Abraham family. I have made occasional reference to copies of documents found in the Portfolio volumes of manuscripts in Friends House Library. These volumes are a miscellany from all periods of Friends' history.

Notes

Page 1	There is a way of making free...Eavan Boland: *In a Time of Violence*, Manchester, 1994, p.35.
Page 9	We acknowledge, O Lord...Jeremiah 14: 20-21.
Page 12	I was born in the year 1614...Margaret Fell, *A Brief Collection of...the Life of Margaret Fell* 1710, p.1.
Page 12	A good market for all kinds...Edward Hughes (ed.), *Sir Daniel Fleming's Description of Cumberland, Westmoreland and Furness 1671*,Cumberland Record Series volume 11, 1961, p. 29.
Page 14	The canal, a mile and a half in length...*Victoria County History of Lancashire*, Volume 8, London, 1993, p.348.
Page 17	The forest and desmesne of Furness...*Victoria County History of Lancashire*, Volume 8, p. 286.
Page 18	*Ecce Agnus Dei*.... Behold the Lamb of God, who takes away the sins of the world. Lord I am not worthy that you should enter under my roof: but speak the word only and my soul will be cleansed.
Page 18	My father's name was John Askew...Margaret Fell, *A Brief Collection of...the Life of Margaret Fell*, p.1.
Page 21	And the people chode...Numbers 20: 3-11 (Geneva text 1560) One of many interesting issues, which I could not explore fully in this book, is the changing nature of religious language. Where I have used the Genevan words it is in the hope of giving the reader the sense of an evolving Protestant tradition. The Authorised (King James) version of the Bible appeared in 1611 and could equally have been read by John Askew.
Page 24	Dalton church: the description is loosely based on what remains of the medieval interior of the church of St Ethelbert in the Suffolk village of Hesset.
Page 25	O Lord our heavenly Father.... This collect is included in the appendix to the Geneva text of the Bible produced in

London by Robert Bakker, printer in 1607. It can be found in the British Library.

Page 25   The Father which in heaven art...This prayer, given the title Lord's Prayer, comes from the same source. It is to be found among a selection of Psalms for which the printer has thoughtfully supplied musical notation 'for the help of those that are desirous to learne to sing'. I do not know its origin.

Page 26   I was brought up and lived with my Father...Margaret Fell, *A Brief Collection of...the Life of Margaret Fell*, p. 1.

Page 27   Handfasted: an exchange of vows before witnesses that amounted to a common law marriage as long as it was consummated. The church would have preferred to see it as a betrothal ceremony.

Page 29   Here is the Spring where waters flow...The foreword to Robert Bakker's Bible (London 1607).

Page 29   ...I was married unto Thomas Fell...Margaret Fell, *A Brief Collection of...the Life of Margaret Fell*, p.1.

Page 31   Labour after a right understanding...quoted Owen Watkins, *The Puritan Experience*, London, 1972, p.8. (Baxter: *Practical Works*, 1838 reprint, vol ii, p. 589.)

Page 33   The first Lord's day being Oct 6...Alan Macfarlane (ed.), *Diary of Ralph Josselin*, London, 1976 p. 7.

Page 39   ...oppressed with feares that she should not doe well on this child...Ibid, p. 50. The year was 1645.

Page 39   How soon, my Dear, death may my steps attend...The poem is quoted in full in E.W. White: *Anne Bradstreet, The Tenth Muse*,New York 1971, p.200. First printed 1678.

Page 39   Look to my little babes, *ibid*.

Page 40   being then in labour of her first Childe..., D.J.H. Clifford (ed.), *Diaries of Anne Clifford*, London, 1990, p.178. The year was 1665.

Page 42   I will lift up mine eyes unto the hills...Psalm 121:1-2.

Page 43   Ne had the apple taken been...Adam Lay Ybounden, a fifteenth century carol.

Page 43-44	And Joseph also went up from Galilee...Luke 2: 4-7. The translation is that of the Geneva Bible. The note reads, 'Whereby appeared his povertie and their cruelty, which would not pitie such a woman in such a case'.
Page 45	The Lord is the portion of mine inheritance...Psalm 16: 5-6.
Page 46-47	Looking down into my father's dead face...Alice Walker: 'Goodnight, Willie Lee, I'll see you in the morning' from *Anything We Love Can Be Saved*, London 1997, p.100.
Page 47	(I) was Inquiring after the way of the Lord...Margaret Fell, *A Brief Collection of...the Life of Margaret Fell*, p 2.
Page 47	God hath taken away a son...Alan Macfarlane (ed.), *The Diary of Ralph Josselin* p.114. The entry is for 1647.
Page 48	Examine yourselves, whether ye be in the faith...2 Corinthians 13: 5-6.
Page 48	Be perfect, be of good comfort...2 Corinthians 13: 11.
Page 49	[Thomas Fell] was a Justice of the Quorum...Margaret Fell, *A Brief Collection of...the Life of Margaret Fell*, p 2.
Page 53	There are certain periods of history...Hugh Trevor Roper, *Archbishop Laud*, London, 1963, introduction.
Page 54	...did traitorously and wickedly counsel his Majesty...Quoted in Barry Williams, *Elusive Settlement, England's Revolutionary years 1637-1701*, London, 1984, p. 37.
Page 56	Shall we receive good at the hand of God...Job 2:10.
Page 56	I was one that sought after the best Things...Margaret Fell, *A Brief Collection of...the Life of Margaret Fell*, p 2.
Page 59	The grass withereth...Isaiah 40:8.
Page 59	Blessed are the merciful...Matthew 5: 7-8.
Page 62	Examine yourselves whether ye be in the faith, 2 Corinthians 13.5.
Page 65	...lo, there was a great earthquake...Revelation 6: 12-13.

Page 66   ...at night my heart settled...Alan Macfarlane (ed.), *Diary of Ralph Josselin*, p.224 (1650).

Page 66-67   Behold, the Tabernacle of God is with men...Revelation 21: 3-4.

Page 68   ...(George Fox) was walking in a field on a First-day morning...John Nickalls (ed.), *Journal of George Fox*, London, 1975 p.7.

Page 71   ...the healing of all our wounds...Alice Walker. See note for p.46-47.

Page 71   ...as many as received him...John 1:12.

Page 74   Examine yourselves...2 Corinthians 13.5

Page 75   This know also...2 Timothy 3:1.

Page 75   Therefore is the anger of the Lorde kindled...Isaiah 5:25.

Page 75   How long wilt thou forget me...Psalm 13:1.

Page 76   ...and then the light and truth...John Nickalls (ed.), *Journal of George Fox* p. 70.

Page 77   The eternal God is thy refuge...Deuteronomy 33:27.

Page 79   I declared the everlasting truth...George Fox, *Journal of George Fox*, edited Daniel Pickard, London, 1891 p. 112.

Page 79   Husband was not at Home...Margaret Fell, *A Brief Collection of...the Life of Margaret Fell*, p. 2.

Page 79   ...would talk of high notions and perfection...George Fox, *Journal*, volume 1 p.119.

Page 80   So at night we had much of reasoning...George Fox, *Journal*, volume I, p.119.

Page 80   ...it pleased the Lord in his Infinite Mercy...Margaret Fell, *A Brief Collection of...the Life of Margaret Fell*, p. 2.

Page 81   Soon after a day was to be observed for a humiliation...George Fox, Journal, Volume 1, p.119.

Page 81-82   And the first words that he spoke...*Quaker Faith and Practice*, London, 1995, 19.07.

Page 84	At Jacob's Well a stranger sought...Closing song from *Lark Rise to Candleford*, two plays by Keith Dewhurst based on Flora Thomson's trilogy, London, 1980.
Page 84	The woman then left her water pot...John 4: 28-29.
Page 85	You will say, *Quaker faith & practice* 19.07. (See note on 'And the first words', p 81-82)
Page 86	And whilst I was sitting...Margaret Fell's testimony to the life of George Fox, printed in George Fox, *Journal of George Fox*, Volume II, p. 513.
Page 86	Art thou that George Fox...George Fox, *Journal*, Volume 1, p. 118.
Page 86-87	...opened Christ's and the apostles' practices...Margaret Fell's testimony to George Fox, George Fox, *Journal*, Volume II, p.514.
Page 87	At Night G. Fox spoke so powerfully...Margaret Fell: *A Brief Collection of...the Life of Margaret Fell*, p. 3.
Page 87	.... thou bread of life...quoted in Isabel Ross: *Margaret Fell, Mother of Quakerism*, York, 1993, p.36/7.
Page 88	...And if I have faith...*I Corinthians* 13:2. (Jerusalem Bible)
Page 90	Fountain of Light...Epistle to All the Professors of the World, 1656, *A Brief Collection of...the Life of Margaret Fell*, p. 73.
Page 91	And if you love the Light...General Epistle to Friends, 1655, ibid, p. 70.
Page 91	Let the Eternal Light search you...Epistle to Convinced Friends, 1656, ibid, p. 91.
Page 91	And on the invisible wait in silence...To Friends, 1654, ibid, p. 53.
Page 91	God hath sent forth the Spirit of his Son...General Epistle to Friends, 1658, ibid, p. 196.
Page 91	Where Christ hath given you Light...Epistle of MF to Friends, 1657, ibid, p. 192.
Page 91	For the woman that hath lost the Groat...To All the Professors of the World, 1656, ibid, p.73.

Page 91	In your measures of the Living Light…Epistle to Friends at Grayrigge, 1655, ibid, p. 68.
Page 92	…this Word which we have seen…An Epistle to Convinced Friends, 1656, ibid, p.91.
Page 92	So God Almighty be your Strength…To Francis Howgill and Thomas Robertson, 1657, ibid, p. 195.
Page 92	Dwell in Love and Unity…An Epistle to Convinced Friends, 1656, ibid, p. 91.
Page 92	but he and his men…Margaret Fell: *A Brief Collection of…the Life of Margaret Fell*, p.3.
Page 92	And Friends your Day of Calling is come…An Epistle to Convinced Friends, 1656, *A Brief Collection of…the Life of Margaret Fell*, p.91.
Page 93	The plaiges of god fall upon thee…George Fox, *Journal* Volume I, p.231 (Quoted Isabel Ross, *Margaret Fell*, p. 27). The date is 1655.
Page 95	The people were quiet…George Fox, Journal, Volume 1, p.132.
Page 95	Mary Akehurst, a religious Woman of Lewis…Joseph Besse: *A Collection of Sufferings of the People called Quakers*, Volume 1, London, 1753. p. 711.
Page 95	Richard Hubberthorn and others…Ibid p. 303.
Page 95	Rebecca Lucas…Ibid p. 665.
Page 96	And I was but young in the Truth…Spence Mss. III, 135 (quoted Isabel Ross, *Margaret Fell Mother of Quakerism*, p.35).
Page 97	There is many in this city…Thomas Holme to Margaret Fell from Chester, end March 1654. No.55 in Geoffrey Nuttall: *Early Quaker Letters, Swarthmore Mss Calendar to 1660*, manuscript copy in Friends House Library.
Page 97	…all this city is on fire…ibid. No.140, Alexander Parker and Francis Howgill to Margaret Fell from London, 3 April 1655.

Page 97-98   You were elected before the foundation of the world
              was...Letter from Margaret Fell to John Stubbs & William
              Caton 1657, (Swarthmore Mss Vol VIII).

Page 98   Even so ye are called in one hope...Epistle to Friends, 1654.
              Margaret Fell, *A Brief Collection of...the Life of Margaret Fell*,
              p. 57.

Page 99   ...my Deare unfained Love...Margaret Fell To GK, 1657,
              Spence Mss, Volume III, No. 47.

Page 100   ...here you are found worshipping the imagination...For
              Manasseth-Ben-Israel. The Call of the Jews out of Babylon,
              1656. Margaret Fell:*A Brief Collection of...the Life of Margaret
              Fell*, p.101.

Page 100   ...some thinke the very world would end in 56...Alan
              Macfarlane, *Diary of Ralph Josselin*, p.360 (26 Jan 1655/6).

Page 102   My fear is of provoking the justice of God...Quoted William
              Braithwaite, *Beginnings of Quakerism*, London, 1912. p. 273.

Page 102   ...and fearfull lyes and storys...Spence Mss, Volume III:135

Page 103   We liv'd together twenty six years...Margaret Fell, *A Brief
              Collection of...the Life of Margaret Fell*, p. 2.

Page 103   ...be faithful unto death...Margaret Fell to Thomas Fell,
              February 1652/3, Abraham Mss 1. (Isabel Ross, *Margaret
              Fell*, p. 119, gives the letter in full.)

Page 104   ...if we should sell the Truth of God...Margaret Fell the
              younger to Thomas Fell and Colonel West, Spence MSS III
              42/43.

Page 104   My dear one, I cannot forget thee...Margaret Fell to George
              Fell (1657),Spence Mss, Volume III, 60. (The letter is given
              in full in Isabel Ross, *Margaret Fell*, p. 22-3.)

Page 104   ...was as tender of me...William Caton, *Life of William
              Caton*, London, 1839, p10.

Page 104   My dear Lamb, my dear Love...Letter to William Caton in
              Holland, 1657, Margaret Fell, *A Brief Collection of...the Life
              of Margaret Fell*, p. 194.

Page 105   Judge Fell was very serviceable...George Fox's preface to the Journal of William Caton, quoted in Isabel Ross, *Margaret Fell*, p. 117.

Page 105   Ye have not chosen me...John 15: 16-20.

Page 106   He Liv'd about six Years after I was convinc'd...Margaret Fell, *A Brief Collection of...the Life of Margaret Fell*, p. 3.

Page 107   ...amongst kings and with a more than regal solemnity...Abraham Cowley quoted in the entry on Cromwell in the *Dictionary of National Biography*, vol 5, Oxford, 1922, p.181.

Page 107   Jesus saith unto her...John 4: 16-17.

Page 109   About this time great stirs were in the nation...George Fox, *Journal*, Volume I, p. 448.

Page 110   29th May 1660: This day came in his Majestie...E. S. de Beer (ed.), *Diary of John Evelyn* Volume III, Oxford, 1955, p. 246.

Page 111   ...some of whom sat in the chimney...George Fox, *Journal*, Volume I, p. 472.

Page 112   And I having a great family...Margaret Fell's Testimony printed, in George Fox, *Journal*, Volume II, p. 516.

Page 112   The woman went her way...John 4: 28.

Page 114   No People can retain God...'Declaration and Information from the People of God called Quakers to the present Governors the King and both Houses of Parliament', Margaret Fell, *A Brief Collection of...the Life of Margaret Fell*, p. 207.

Page 114   Treason, Treachery and false Dealing...ibid , p. 210.

Page 116   There is a spirit which I feel...quoted in William Braithwaite, *Beginnings of Quakerism*, p. 275.

Page 117   ...the Fifth-Monarchy-Men raised an Insurrection... Margaret Fell, *A Brief Collection of...the Life of Margaret Fell*, p. 5.

Page 117   On 24th, at Swarthmore...Joseph Besse, *A Collection of the Sufferings of the People Called Quakers*, volume I, p. 308.

Page 117	...if the things continue that they keep men in custody...Bridget Fell to Margaret Fell (Feb 1661), quoted in Helen Crosfield: *Margaret Fox of Swarthmoor Hall*, London, 1913, p. 89-90.
Page 118	Our principle is, and our practices have always been...George Fox, *Journal*, volume I, p. 494-5.
Page 119	...had Freedom in Spirit...Margaret Fell, *A Brief Collection of...the Life of Margaret Fell*, p. 5.
Page 120	...then as they are moved of the Lord...Margaret Fell, Epistle on Marriage, 1656, Swarthmore Mss, Volume VIII.
Page 121	...and then I was moved of the Lord...Margaret Fell, *A Brief Collection of...the Life of Margaret Fell*, p. 5.
Page 122	On the 28th of October the Meetings...Joseph Besse, *A Collection of the Sufferings of the People Called Quakers*, volume I, p. 388.
Page 122	...I say unto you, That ye resist not evil...Matthew 5: 39.
Page 123	Let Faith, Hope and Charity...Epistle to Friends 1661, Margaret Fell, *A Brief Collection of...the Life of Margaret Fell*, p. 272.
Page 124	I was moved of the Lord again...Margaret Fell, *A Brief Collection of...the Life of Margaret Fell*, p. 6.
Page 125	...we are no such people...Isabel Ross, *Margaret Fell*, p. 164.
Page 125	I gave you an account in my last...Norman Penney (ed.), *Extracts from State Papers*, London, 1913, p. 188-9.
Page 126	Swear not at all...Matthew 5: 34-7.
Page 128	...I am here this Day upon this Account, to bear Testimony to the Truth. This and the quotations which follow come from Margaret Fell's account of her trial in Margaret Fell, *A Brief Collection of...the Life of Margaret Fell*, p. 277ff.
Page 129	Who shall separate us from the love of Christ...Romans 8: 35.
Page 130	I am present with you...Epistle to Friends that were Prisoners in Lancaster, 1654. Margaret Fell, *A Brief Collection of...the Life of Margaret Fell*, p. 59.

Page 130	So dear Hearts, ye are purged…Epistle to all Friends Prisoners at London and Bristol and elsewhere in 1664, Margaret Fell, *A Brief Collection of…the Life of Margaret Fell*, p. 302.
Page 131	What Laws have you made or changed…Letter sent to the King from prison 1666, Margaret Fell, *A Brief Collection of…the Life of Margaret Fell*, p. 325.
Page 132	(Mary's) spirit near and dear and present with me…Swarthmore Mss Volume I, 101, Isabel Ross, *Margaret Fell*, p. 187.
Page 133	…being seduced into that Phanatique opinion…Norman Penney (ed.), *Extracts from State Papers*, p. 227.
Page 134-39	…Whereas it hath been an objection…and the quotations which follow from *Women's Speaking Justified* are taken from: Christine Trevett (ed.), *Women's Speaking Justified*, London, 1989, p. 4ff
Page 141	…thy mother's slights of me…The full text of the letter is given in Isabel Ross, *Margaret Fell*, p. 206-210
Page 143	…and gave open testimonies…Swarthmore Ms 1,108, Isabel Ross: *Margaret Fell*, p.212.
Page 143	And then it was Eleven years…Margaret Fell, *A Brief Collection of…the Life of Margaret Fell*, p. 8.
Page 143-144	I had seen from the Lord…George Fox, *Journal*, volume II, p. 117.
Page 144	And the bride, the Lamb's wife…Christine Trevett (ed.), *Women's Speaking Justified*, p. 11.
Page 145	…we took each other…George Fox, *Journal*, volume II, p. 118.
Page 145	…And likewise the saide Margaret…Marriage Certificate, Thirnbeck Mss 7.
Page 145	…Husband stayed…Margaret Fell, *A Brief Collection of…the Life of Margaret Fell*l, p. 9.
Page 145	I travelled through Wiltshire…George Fox, *Journal*, volume II, p. 118-119.

Page 146	...if thou would leave Lancashire...John Rous to Margaret Fell (dated, 25th 10th month 1669), Journal of the Friends Historical Society, volume 30, 1933, p. 35.
Page 146	...she was haled out of her house...George Fox, *Journal*, volume II, p. 120.
Page 146	...where I continued a whole Year...Margaret Fell, *A Brief Collection of...the Life of Margaret Fell*, p. 9.
Page 148	And she brought forth a man child...Revelation 12: 5-6.
Page 149	Friends are generally well...George Fox: *Journal*, volume II, p.160.
Page 150	Concerning the women's meetings...George Fox, 'An Exhortation to set up women's meetings', 1666, Christine Trevett (ed.), *Women's Speaking Justified*, p. 19.
Page 151	...and in your day's work...*Epistle from Women's Yearly Meeting at York, 1688*, Augustan Reprint Society, University of California, 1979.
Page 151	Mary Gore's daughter...*Some minutes of the Women's MM at Hardshaw* (1693-9), Portfolio Mss 31. 12. Dated from 1693-1699.
Page 152	....pd of the weomens Meetinge stocke to ffriends of Hawxheade Meettinge...Norman Penney (ed.), *The Household Account Book of Sarah Fell*, Cambridge, 1920, p.29.
Page 153	...pd of the weomens stocke...to Ann Birkett...Ibid, p.179.
Page 153	That the young ones when they feel the Lord...Epistle signed by Susannah Ingram, Mary Lower, Isabelle Morice, Sarah Mead and other women. Box Meeting Ms 15 (dated c1697 by Isabel Ross)
Page 153	And now Dear Friend we are truly comforted...London Quarterly Women's Meeting to Margaret Fell, 1695. Spence III, 195.
Page 153-154	We, being met together in fear of the Lord...*Epistle from the Women's Yearly Meeting at York 1688*: Augustan Reprint Society, University of California, 1979.
Page 154	And therefore dear Friends and Sisters...*Epistle from the*

Women's Yearly Meeting at York, 1698. Quoted in: Quaker Women's Group, *Bringing the Invisible into the Light*, London, 1986, p.8.

Page 155   Dear Heart, Thou seemedst to be a little grieved...George Fox, *Journal*, volume II, p. 206.

Page 155   [He] fell sick...ibid, p. 518.

Page 156   After this, the said George Fox's Wife...Joseph Besse, *A Collection of the Sufferings of the People called Quakers*, volume II, p. 75.

Page 156   ...and I was very desirous...Margaret Fox's testimony to George Fox in George Fox, *Journal*, volume II, p. 518.

Page 157-158   Dear Heart...the road...George Fox, *Journal*, volume II, p. 258.

Page 157   ...he was but weakly...Margaret Fell, *A Brief Collection of...the Life of Margaret Fell*, p. 9.

Page 158   What canst thou say? *Quaker faith & practice* 19.07.

Page 159   Dear and faithful; whom ye Lord hath chosen...Margaret Fox to William Penn, 1677, Portfolio Mss 36: 33.

Page 159   Out of Sion, the Perfection of Beauty...and the quotations that follow on pages 159-161: Margaret Fell, *Daughter of Sion Awakened*, 1677, in Margaret Fell, *A Brief Collection of...the Life of Margaret Fell*, p. 510ff.

Page 162   ...I went to Swarthmore...George Fox, *Journal*, Volume II, p. 335.

Page 163   ...and this is as full and plaine an acct...Sarah Meade to Margaret Fox, 1683, Abraham Mss 26.

Page 164   I was about six hours in travail...Sarah Meade to Margaret Fox, May 1684. The full text is given in *Journal of Friends Historical Society*, volume 30, p. 42 and in Isabel Ross, *Margaret Fell*, p.351.

Page 165   1683: Margaret Fox, for suffering Meetings...Joseph Besse, *A Collection of the Sufferings of the People called Quakers*, volume I, p. 326.

Page 166   So I was moved to go to London...Margaret Fell, *A Brief Collection of...the Life of Margaret Fell*, p.10.

Page 166   Be pleased to Remember...Thirnbeck Mss JFHS vol ix p143-4 Margaret Fox to King Charles, 1684, *Journal of Friends Historical Society*, volume 9, p. 143-4.

Page 167   Not from any want of tenderness...Quoted in Barry Williams, *Elusive Settlement, England's Revolutionary Years, 1637-1701*, p. 191.

Page 168   The tithe of Corn taken...Joseph Besse, *A Collection of Sufferings of the People called Quakers*, volume I, p. 330.

Page 168   Walk wisely and circumspectly...quoted in William Braithwaite, *Second Period of Quakerism*, p.160.

Page 168   The Quaker, too...G.M.Trevelyan, *English Social History*, London, 1958, p. 295.

Page 169   And now God has placed thee over us...Margaret Fox to King William, Margaret Fell, *A Brief Collection of...the Life of Margaret Fell*, p. 532.

Page 169   ...better in his health and strength...Margaret Fox's testimony to George Fox, George Fox, *Journal*, volume II, p. 519.

Page 169   ...my Heart was rejoyced...Epistle to the Women's Meeting in London, 1690, Margaret Fell, *A Brief Collection of...the Life of Margaret Fell*, p. 14.

Page 169-170   ...so that we were very willing...Margaret Fox's testimony to George Fox, George Fox, *Journal*, volume II, p. 519.

Page 170   And ye now therefore have sorrow...John 16:22.

Page 170   'whatever he hath yet' Margaret Fox's testimony to George Fox, George Fox, *Journal*, volume II, p. 519.

Page 171   For I know his faithfulness...Margaret Fox's testimony to George Fox, George Fox, *Journal*, volume II, p. 519.

Page 171   ...silly poor gospel...Margaret Fox, Epistle to Friends, 1700, Ms Portfolio 25.66. (Quaker Faith and Practice: 20.31)

Page 172   Dear Friends, Brethren and Sisters...Margaret Fox, Epistle to Friends, 1700, Ms Portfolio 25.66.